Contents

I | Sorting living things

1.1 Ten questions

a Work in small groups. One person thinks of an animal and the others can ask up to ten questions to find out what it is. They can only ask questions with a 'yes' or 'no' answer.

b After you have tried to guess each person's animal, work out which questions give the most useful answers. For example, which is it better to start with: 'Does it have green eyes?' or 'Does it have fur?' Why?

c Write down ten 'useful' questions.

d Put them in order with the most useful first.

e Explain why you have put your questions in that order.

f Repeat the game, but make up your own list this time. Does it work?

1.2 Making groups

goldfish ant sparrow cod magpie carrot deer
bee stone bear shrimp car lettuce robin
monkey snake matchstick potato human being slug

Put the things in this list into groups. You can use up to six groups.

a Write down the list of things in each group.

b Give each group a title.

c Say what the things in each group have in common.

d Your teacher may have brought an object for you to look at. What group would you put it in? Explain how you decided.

1.3 Scientific names

Use the classification diagram in *Active Science 1* (pages 134–5) to answer these questions:

a What is being classified on pages 134–5?

b Which group are amphibia in?

c Describe an amphibian.

d What is the scientific name for plants which have leaves and stems but no roots?

e Give three examples of animals that are arthropods.

f What do arthropods have in common?

g Which group are you in?

1.4 Don't fall into the trap

The diagram shows a pitfall trap. It catches insects that run along the surface of the ground. Insects that fall into the trap cannot get out.

You need:
– trowel
– empty yoghurt pot
– hand lens
– flat piece of stiff plastic or card

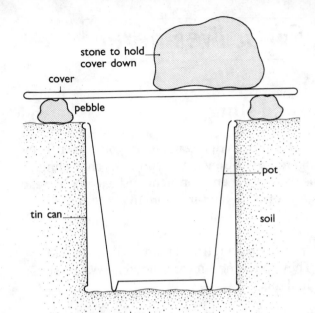

A pitfall trap

A problem

a If you trap a large carnivorous beetle and some smaller insects, you will end up with one well fed, contented beetle! How can you stop the beetle eating the insects and spoiling your results? Think of a solution to this problem. Then explain it to your teacher.

Investigating

b Use the trap to investigate one of these problems:
● Are the insects that are active in the daytime the same types that are active at night?
● Where do you find the widest range of insects? You will need to identify your catch. Look very carefully at your insects. You may find a hand lens (magnifying glass) helpful. Then use the drawings to find your insect's name.
● What else might affect where insects live? Test your idea.

Some animals you may find in your pitfall trap (not drawn to scale)

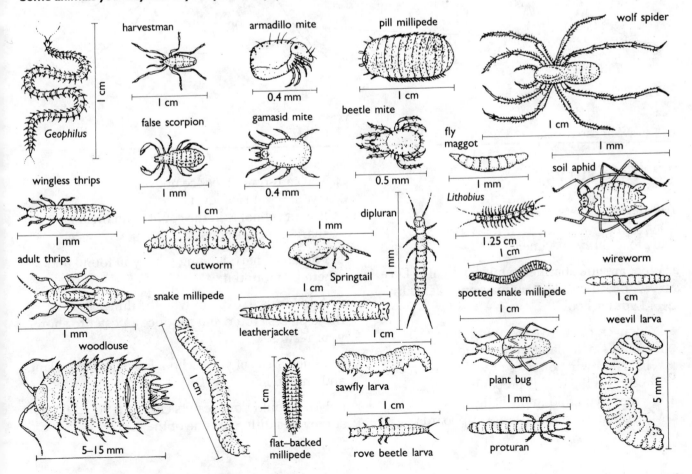

2.1 Itch and sting

Human fleas are insects that can live on your head. They are not dangerous, but they make you itch! They cling to hairs in this warm, safe environment and eat bits of dead skin. People with clean hair are more likely to catch fleas than people with dirty hair.

Wasps are insects that can travel many kilometres to find food. They collect nectar from flowers. Wasps sting if they are in danger.

Look carefully at the drawings.

Observing

a How is the flea adapted to its life in human hair?

b How is the wasp adapted to its life?

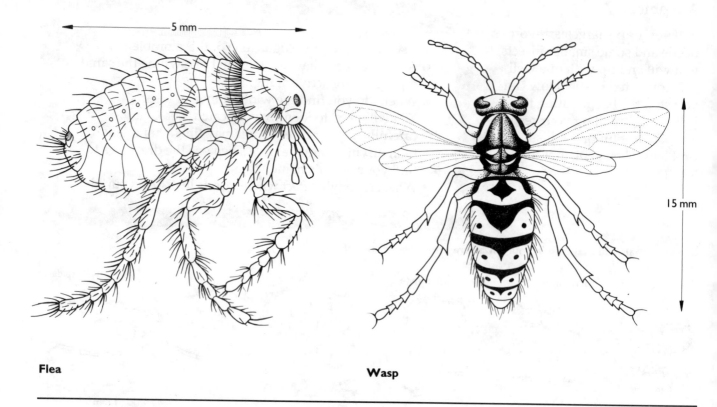

— 5 mm —

15 mm

Flea

Wasp

2.2 Life survey

You need:
– hand lens
– key to identify specimens

a What are you sharing your school with? Do a survey to find out what animals and plants live round your school.

- Look in cracks between paving stones.
- Look for small plants at the bottom of walls.
- What is growing on trees or walls? (A green smudge on the wall is probably an alga.)
- What can you find in the hedges?
- Mice often live at the back of cupboards.
- You can sometimes see house-martins or swallows at roof level.
- If your school is in the country, an owl may be sharing the outhouse!

b Prepare a map showing what you found and where you found it.

c Add labels to explain why the things live in those places. You could produce a poster to show your results.

d Which areas of your school have the most plant and animal life?

e How would your results change if you did your survey at a different time of the year?

© Gott, Price, Thornley/Collins Educational 1992   *KS 3 Assessment Activities Pack A*

2.3 Getting the bird

Parrots are birds that live in rainforests. If a parrot escapes from a zoo and flies off, it will not survive long. Why is this? Write down all the reasons you can think of.

2.4 An apple for the teacher

In September, Cyril Creep brought an apple for his new science teacher. She was very pleased; she ate the apple and told Cyril to plant the pips. He watered them and kept them warm. But they did not grow.
Cyril had a brainwave. He thought, 'Perhaps apple seeds only grow in the spring, after a cold spell.' His teacher told him to investigate.

This is what he did. He collected 60 pips from the same apple tree. He kept 30 of them in a freezer for three weeks and then planted them. The other 30 pips were planted straight away. Here are his results:

	Number germinated
From freezer	25
Straight from tree	3

a How many seeds from the freezer did not germinate?

b Why did he collect all the seeds from the same tree?

c You have to grow your own apple tree. How should you look after the seeds? When should you plant them?

d How many seeds should you plant? Explain your answer.

Planning

e Write a plan for an investigation to find out the best time and temperature to keep apple seeds before planting them.

2.5 And today's mystery object is ...

Observing

Look carefully at the animal or plant your teacher has shown you.

a Work in a group. Suggest six places you might expect to find it and why.

b Then, on your own, choose one of the places and say why you think the plant or animal would live there.

3 Cycles

3.1 Where there's muck ...

Gardeners with small gardens often buy a compost bin. It saves space and looks tidy.

Look at the bin designs here.

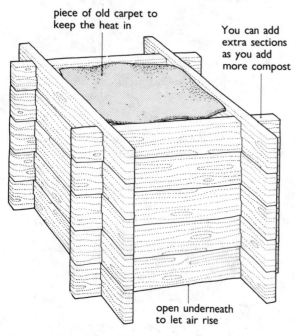

a Wooden-frame bin

piece of old carpet to keep the heat in

You can add extra sections as you add more compost

open underneath to let air rise

a Make a list of the good and bad points of each design.

b Which do you think is the best? Why?

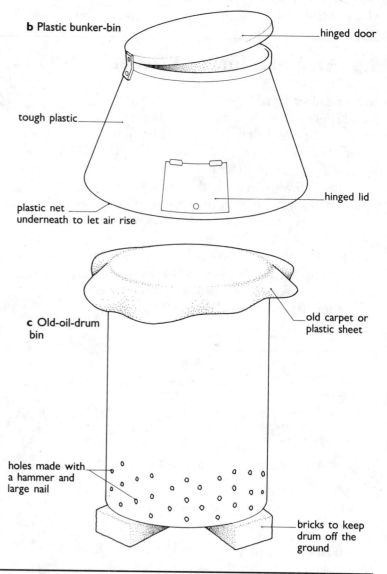

b Plastic bunker-bin

hinged door

tough plastic

hinged lid

plastic net underneath to let air rise

c Old-oil-drum bin

old carpet or plastic sheet

holes made with a hammer and large nail

bricks to keep drum off the ground

3.2 Blooming farmers!

Planning

a The water company asked its scientists to find out which had a bigger effect on the growth of the algae:
– the fertiliser, or
– the high temperature.
Write a plan they could follow.

b Explain how the results from the investigation would show who was right – the water company or the environmental group?

Warning to visitors - poisonous algae!

Anglian Water has warned visitors to Rutland Water to avoid any contact with the greenish scum round the edge of the lake. The scum is a type of poisonous blue-green alga. A dog has already died from drinking water from the lake. The water company says there is no danger to drinking supplies because they filter out the algae before any water is piped to homes.

The chairperson of the local environmental group said 'This poisonous growth is a direct result of farmers using too much fertiliser. The fertilisers wash through the soil into the lake and cause the sudden growth of the algae. We must act quickly before someone dies.'

The local farmers and the water board itself deny there is a crisis. They blame the unusually hot weather for the algae.

KS 3 Assessment Activities Pack A

3.3 Strong enough?

Investigating

Are biodegradable bags strong enough?

a Plan and carry out an investigation to find out if biodegradable bags are as strong as ordinary ones.

You need: – plastic bags
– weights
– scissors

3.4 Farmer Green had a farm ... AS 3

I like to keep my cows out in the field for most of the year. I don't have to put up expensive buildings or pay the cost of heating and lighting them. The cows add their own sort of fertiliser to my fields! I also use organic fertilisers on all my fields and change the crops I grow so that the ground has some time to rest. I never burn the left-overs after I have harvested. I plough them back into the ground to make it richer for next year's crop.

I use modern methods to produce more food more cheaply. I keep my cows in heated buildings and feed them special concentrated foods. I use antibiotics to keep them healthy and chemicals to make them grow faster. The waste they produce is taken away in tanker lorries. To keep my fields free of plant diseases, I burn the stubble after the harvest. I take good care of my cows and feed them well.

Farmer Grey

Farmer Green

a Work in pairs. One person should pretend to be Farmer Green; the other person should be Farmer Grey. Imagine you meet at a farm show. You start to argue about whose farming methods are better. Act out the argument – but don't come to blows!

b After your argument write down:
– the good and bad points in Green's methods.
– the good and bad points in Grey's methods.

c Which type of farming uses the nitrogen cycle better (See *Active Science 3*, page 95)? Why?

d Which type of farming is better for
– the farmer? Why?
– the person who eats the food? Why?
– the environment? Why?

3.5 Old fossils

'My dad says his physics teacher was an old fossil.' Not yet. But he might be in several million years.

a What would have to happen to make the teacher into a real fossil?

b Draw a cartoon strip to show what happens.

4 Energy flow

4.1 Anyone for eggs?

So many people want eggs that we farm hens like a crop. Many farmers keep them in batteries (rows of cages). A battery hen has a good life in one way – it has food and water when it needs it – but it cannot move about. This means that the hen wastes less of its food on movement so that it converts more to meat. Some people think this is cruel. Others think the hen does not mind.

Here is some information about chicken farming:

Farming system	Number of birds in 4 square metres
free-range	1
intensive but with a lot of straw	28
intensive with little straw	88
most intensive battery system	96

a A farmer has a chicken house with a floor space of 20 square metres. How many birds could he keep with the:
– free-range system?
– most intensive system?

b Four square metres is 40 000 cm². How much of the area of your sheet of paper would a battery chicken have in the most intensive system? Draw a rectangle on your paper if it will fit.

c Prepare an advertisement for an animal rights campaign. Show that battery farming does not give the chickens enough space. Include a chart showing the data in the table. Choose a chart which you think shows this best: a line graph, a bar chart or a pie chart.

d Design a battery cage. In your design, explain how you would deal with food, water, droppings and eggs.

Planning

e Some people say that battery hens produce eggs with very thin shells that break in the box. Plan an investigation to test this.

f Can you think of any reasons they might be thin? Write a plan to test your idea.

g What do you think about battery farming?
● On your own, write down your views. Make sure you think of arguments for *and* against.
● Hold a class discussion about battery farming.
● On your own, look back at the opinions you held before the class discussion. Have they changed? Write down any changes and explain what made you change your mind.

KS 3 Assessment Activities Pack A

12 Human impact on the Earth

12.1 Pollution across frontiers

The table shows how much sulphur is given out by factories and power stations every year for countries in Europe. It also shows the sulphur deposited as acid rain etc. in each country

You can see which European countries pollute the atmosphere badly. They produce a lot of sulphur dioxide, which makes acid rain. The table also shows the countries which receive most acid rain.

a Which country is the most polluted by acid rain?

b Which country is the worst sulphur dioxide polluter?

c Which countries give out more sulphur than is deposited inside their borders?

d Which countries take in the sulphur that comes from these countries?

The Swedish government has given millions of pounds to Poland and Yugoslavia to help clean up their industries.

e Why did they do this rather than spending it on Swedish factories?

Country	Given out	Deposited
	(thousands of tonnes of sulphur)	
Belgium	404	193
Denmark	228	131
Finland	270	352
France	1800	1454
Germany	3816	2324
Ireland	88	76
Italy	2200	1358
Netherlands	240	208
Norway	76	306
Poland	2150	1596
Portugal	84	88
Spain	1000	700
Sweden	275	566
Switzerland	58	169
UK	2560	1016

12.2 Changes at home

Work in a group. Your teacher will provide some old maps. Use them to see how your town or village has changed over the last 200 years. You could also talk to local people about their memories.

a Make a list of what has changed.

b Why have these changes happened?

c Which changes have made things better?

d Which changes have made things worse?

e Predict what changes might happen in the next 100 years. Say how they may affect the people living then.

f Produce a tourist leaflet about the history of your town or village. Each person in your group should be responsible for one article in the leaflet.

KS 3 Assessment Activities Pack A

4.2 Game parks

Game parks are areas where hunters cannot kill wild animals. The government of Kenya manages the Serengeti Park carefully so that visitors can see some of the most beautiful animals in the world roaming free. The Serengeti covers an area of roughly 38 000 km².

The food web below shows some of the important animals in the Serengeti.

Serengeti Game Park food web

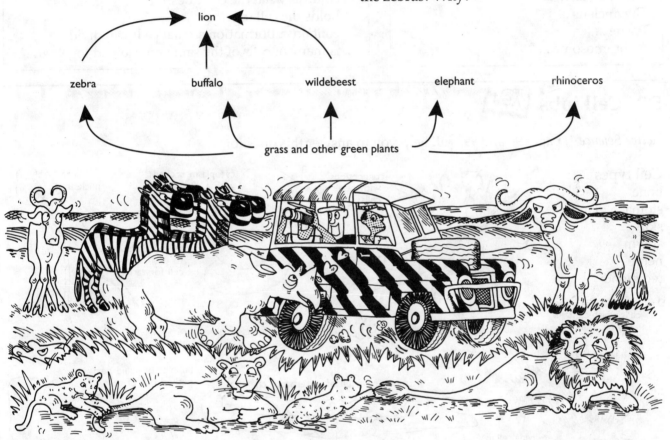

a Which animals do lions eat?

b Which animals eat grass?

c A drought would reduce the amount of grass in the park.
What effect would this have on the animals in the park? Explain your answer carefully.

d A disease has reduced the number of wildebeest. How would this affect
– the lions? Why?
– the zebras? Why?

Animal	Number in 1000 km²
lion	20
wildebeest	6400
zebra	4800
buffalo	600
elephant	32
rhinoceros	2

Animal	Average adult mass (kg)
lion	300
wildebeest	230
zebra	230
buffalo	550
elephant	3200
rhinoceros	2000

Use the data in the tables to answer the following questions.

e Which is the commonest animal in the Serengeti?

f Which is the rarest animal in the Serengeti?

g There are about 750 lions in the Serengeti Park. Work out the total mass of all the lions.

h About how many zebras are there in the Serengeti?

i Work out the total mass of all the zebras.

j Explain why the total mass of zebras is much bigger than the total mass of lions.

5.1 In the cells

Active Science 1, pages 98 and 99, will help you to answer this question.

a Pair up each name in list A with the phrase in list B that describes what it does. Write down the sentences.

A: Names of cells or parts of a cell The cell wall or membrane ... The cytoplasm ... The nucleus ... Tissue ... A chromosome ...	**B: What the parts in list A do** ... makes and stores chemicals in a cell. ... controls what the cell does. ... holds the cell together. ... contains information so that cells can divide. ... is many of cells of the same type joined together.

5.2 Cell jobs [AS 1]

Active Science 1, pages 98 and 99, will help you to answer this question.

Cell types
bone
stomach gland
skin
sperm
nerve
red blood

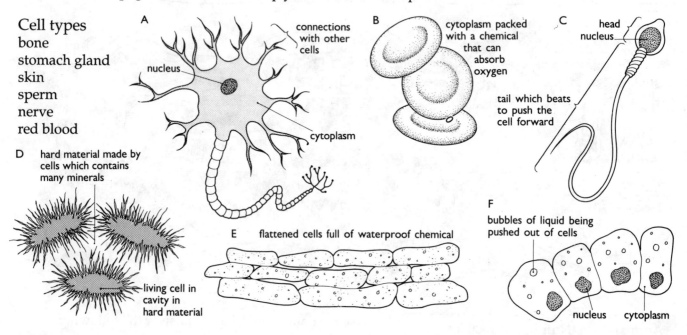

a Draw a table like the one below in your book. Use the cell drawings to fill in the rest of the table.

Drawing	Cell type	The job it does	Why I picked this cell type
A	nerve	Passes messages from one cell to the next cell	It has long strands that connect with the cells.
		Carries oxygen round the body in the blood stream	
		Swims towards the egg to fertilise it	
		Makes and repairs bone	
		Protects the body	
		Produces a chemical to break down food	

5.3 Doctor Frankenstein's shopping list

Doctor Frankenstein has sent Igor shopping for body parts to sew together to make a human being.

Body job no. 118
6 eggs
bones (assorted)
heart
1 kg of flour
5 litres of blood (fresh!)
lungs (from a non-smoker)
brain (medium)
muscles (assorted, good quality)
gut
reproductive organs (female)
1 kg sugar
two eyes (same colour if possible)
one matching pair of ears
hair
skin (about 2.5 m²)
500 g margarine

a The eggs, flour, sugar and margarine are to make a sponge cake. Why does Doctor Frankenstein need all the other things? List the parts he has ordered and say what job each one does in the body.

b Pick two of the items on Frankenstein's list and explain in detail how they keep his monster alive. Explain how the structure of each part helps it to do its job.

5.4 Growing bodies

a Look at the bar graph. How much energy does a 4-year-old boy need?

b How much energy does a 16-year-old girl need?

c Write down two patterns that the chart shows.

d Write a sentence to explain each of the patterns.

e Why do all children need energy?

f What do we call the process the body uses to get energy from sugar?

g Do you stop needing energy when you stop growing? Explain your answer.

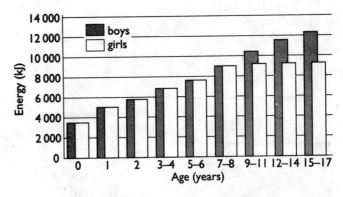

Daily energy needs of boys and girls

5.5 Alive, alive-Oh!

Active Science 1, pages 136–41, may help you with this question.
Here is part of an old biology book:

It is easy to list the things that show us that animals are alive: they move about, they eat, they have babies and they react to changes in their environment. Living organisms are different from non-living objects because they:
– move,
– feed,
– respire,
– excrete,
– grow,
– reproduce,
– respond to changes.

Use this information to say how you know if the objects **a – f** are alive or not. Take care to write a full answer!

a A rabbit

b A doll that wets itself

c A daffodil

d A virus (e.g. one that causes measles)

e A tapeworm

f A radio-controlled car

6 Reproduction

6.1 Flower structure

You need:
– selection of flowers
– scalpel ⚠
– hand lens

a Choose a flower and make three different drawings of it. Each drawing should show a different view. They could be:
– an outside view,
– a close-up of a part of the plant,
– a view of the flower cut open.

b On separate pieces of paper make labels for the parts that:
– attract insects,
– grow into seeds or fruits (the female parts),
– produce pollen (the male parts),
– hold the flower upright,
– protect the flower when it is a bud,
– collect the pollen from other flowers,
Put in any more labels you think are important.

c Swap with your friend. Put the labels in the right place on their drawings. How many did you get right?

d Draw a strip cartoon to show how flowering plants reproduce. Choose any plant you like. Make sure you show the cell stage.

6.2 Dear Aunt ...,

Readers sent these letters to the problem page of a magazine. Some are wrong, some are very wrong! Write a short reply to each question.

Dear Sally

I thought that I couldn't get pregnant because it was a full moon. Was I right? *(Romantic of Wigan)*

We only make love standing up so it must be all right, mustn't it. *(Footsore of Frensham)*

Men need to make love every day: women can only do it once a month. *(Confused of Milton Keynes)*

I'm desperate for a baby. When should we make love? *(Broody of Surbiton)*

6.3 All change

Growing up involves many changes. Puberty is a time when glands in the body start to produce chemicals.

a What changes do these chemicals cause?

b Which changes are permanent?

KS 3 Assessment Activities Pack A

6.4 Play away

Your 3-year-old sister is just starting at play school.
The school takes children from 9 o'clock in the morning until
3 o'clock in the afternoon. The drawing above shows the
school at about 11 o'clock in the morning.

a What do you think the school needs to provide for your sister
during the day? Make a list of important points.

b List the good things about the play school.

c List the bad things about the play school.

7 Good health

7.1 Diphtheria

Diphtheria is a disease caused by bacteria. Children who get it have a fever and problems with breathing and swallowing. Diphtheria used to be one of the biggest causes of death among young children.

Look at the graph and answer these questions:

a When was the diphtheria death rate highest?

b When did the immunisation campaign begin?

c What effect did the campaign have?

d Two doctors were arguing about immunisation against diphtheria.

Immunisation is a dangerous waste of time. There are too many risks of side effects. Parents should not let their children be immunised. We do not need immunisation.

Immunisation has saved thousands of lives. My children have been immunised. I don't want them to take the risk of catching something as dangerous as diphtheria.

Explain how both doctors could use evidence from the graph to support their ideas. What evidence is there that immunisation is a dangerous waste of time?

7.2 Accidents

Use pages 22–3 of *Active Science 2* to answer these questions. Find the information you need before answering.

a How many deaths are the result of accidents at work every year?

b How many people, over 65 years old, died in fires at home in 1986?

c Many people die from falling at home. Which people are most at risk? Why?

d Can you suggest a reason for this pattern?

e Find information about the number of road accidents. Describe any patterns you can see on the chart. Suggest an explanation for each pattern.

7.3 Dangerous drugs

In 1986, a survey asked 14-year-olds about drugs. Their answers were:

Drug	Which have you tried?	Which is most dangerous?
cigarettes	60%	14%
cannabis	7%	3%
heroin	3%	71%
solvents	8%	3%
alcohol	85%	8%
none/don't know	10%	1%

a What percentage of those surveyed have tried glue sniffing?

b What percentage think heroin is the most dangerous drug?

c Over 80% of those asked have tried one of the drugs. Which one?

d Use the information in the tables to decide which drug is the most dangerous. Give reasons for your choice.

e List five ways the drugs in the tables can damage the body.

Drug	Estimated deaths per year
cigarettes	80 000
cannabis	not known
heroin	about 100
solvents	about 130
alcohol	25 000 to 40 000

Drug	Estimated regular users
cigarettes	12 million
cannabis	1.5 million
heroin	100 000
solvents	24 500
alcohol	20 million

7.4 How the other half dies

a What is the most common cause of death in an economically developed country?

b Give two differences between the causes of death in developed and developing countries.

c Explain each of these differences.

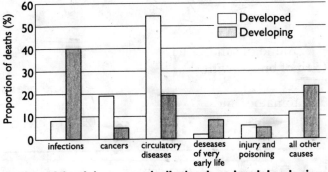

Causes of death in economically developed and developing countries

7.5 How healthy are you?

Here are some questions from a health quiz in a magazine.

a Work in a group to complete more questions for the quiz:
● Write at least six more questions.
● Work out a scoring system for the answers. People who are very healthy should get high scores.

b On your own use all the questions to check your health:
● Work out your own score, and the maximum score.
● Make a plan to improve your health.
  – What should you do?
  – What should you stop doing?

c At home you could:
● Try your quiz on your family and friends. How healthy are they?
● Prepare charts for them to show how they can improve their health.

1 What did you have for breakfast?
  a Nothing
  b A cup of tea or coffee
  c Cereal
  d Brown bread toast
2 How much sugar do you have in hot drinks?
  a More than 1 spoonful
  b Less than 1 spoonful
  c None
3 How often do you eat meat?
  a Every day
  b Most days
  c Never
4 How much alcohol do you drink each day?
  a 4 pints of beer or more (or 4 glasses of wine)
  b 1-3 pints of beer
  c Less than 1 pint of beer
  d None

8.1 Energy in food

This is the energy you get from 100 grams of some foods:

Food (100 g)	Energy content (kJ)
baked beans	300
carrots	100
tomatoes	60
lettuce	40
peanuts	2370
bread	1010
salad dressing	3200
cheddar cheese	1726

a Display this information for a magazine article about foods and diets. Use a pie chart, a line graph or a bar chart, whichever you think is best.

b Which of the snacks below gives you the least energy?

c Where does the energy stored in these foods come from in the first place?

d How would your answer to **c** be different for a pork chop? Explain carefully.

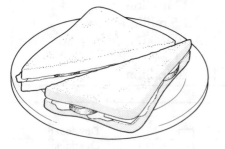

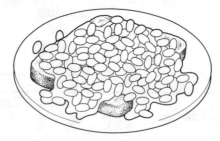

– A round of sandwiches (50 g of bread) with 20 g lettuce, 50 g tomatoes and 30 g of cheese.

– Baked beans (50 g) on one slice of toast (25 g of bread).

– Grated carrot (30 g), sliced tomatoes (50 g), peanuts (30 g) with salad dressing (10 g).

8.2 Tommy rot

A farmer decided to add some extra carbon dioxide gas to the air in her greenhouses. She thought this might increase the mass of tomatoes the plants produced. This is what happened:

	Without extra carbon dioxide	With extra carbon dioxide
Mass of tomatoes produced per plant (kg)	4.4	6.4

a How much extra tomato fruit did the farmer get from each plant?

b She had 30 rows of 50 plants in the greenhouse. How much extra fruit did she get altogether?

c It cost the farmer £20 to add the carbon dioxide. She could sell the tomatoes for 50 p per kilogram. Did she make any extra profit from the experiment?

d Why did adding carbon dioxide help the plants to grow?

e What else is needed for a good crop of tomatoes?

f What gas do the tomato plants give out during the day?

8.3 Greenhouse design

You need:
- 2 large, clear, plastic lemonade bottles
- seedlings in pots
- scissors ⚠
- material for shading the plants

If you have not got the equipment, you could write a plan to say what you would do.

Cut the plastic bottles in half carefully. Use the bottom halves. Each half is a mini-greenhouse.

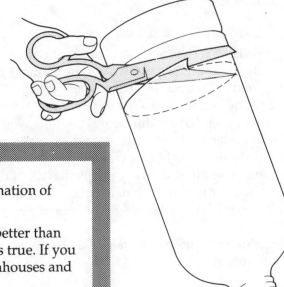

Investigating

a Use your mini-greenhouse to find the best combination of warmth and light for growing plants.

b Some people say glass greenhouses grow plants better than plastic ones. Plan an investigation to find out if this is true. If you can, try out your plan using one of your plastic greenhouses and a clear glass jar.

c Explain why plants grow better in your mini-greenhouse.

8.4 Houseplant fertilisers

a Which fertiliser supplies *most* nitrogen?

b Which fertiliser supplies *least* potassium?

c Can you see any difference between Garden Scenter and Green Magic?

d What do plants use minerals for (See *Active Science 3*, page 66) ?

Little Eco
for all Houseplants
NPK fertiliser 10.5: 4.4:1
Nitrogen (N) total 10.5%
Phosphorus pentoxide (P_2O_5)
soluble in water 4.4% (P 1.9%)
Potassium oxide (K_2O)
soluble in water 1.7% (K 1.1%)

Hortipak Cactus Fertiliser
NPK fertiliser 8:34:32
Nitrogen (N) total 8%
Phosphorus pentoxide (P_2O_5)
soluble in water 34% (P 15%)
Potassium oxide (K_2O)
soluble in water 32% (K 26.5%)
Magnesium oxide (MgO) 370 mg/kg (Mg 222 mg/kg)
Iron (Fe) 170 mg/kg Manganese (Mn) 85 mg/kg
Copper (Cu) 85 mg/kg Zinc (Zn) 30 mg/kg
Boron (B) 45 mg/kg Molybdenum (Mo) 1 mg/kg
100 gram

Green Magic for indoor plants
NPK fertiliser 6:4:4
Nitrogen (N) total 6%
Phosphorus pentoxide (P_2O_5)
soluble in water 3.9% (1.7% P)
Potassium oxide (K_2O)
soluble in water 4% (K 3.3%)
70 ml e

Garden Scenter Houseplant Feed
NPK fertiliser 6:4:4
Nitrogen (N) total 6%
Phosphorus pentoxide
soluble in water 3.9% (1.7% P)
Potassium oxide (K_2O)
soluble in water 4% (3.3% K)
120 ml e

Hortipak African Violet Fertiliser
NPK fertiliser 12:36:14
Nitrogen (N) total 12%
Phosphorus pentoxide (P_2O_5)
soluble in water 36% (P 15.7%)
Potassium oxide (K_2O)
soluble in water 14% (K 11.6%)
Magnesium oxide (MgO) 370 mg/kg (Mg 222 mg/kg)
Iron (Fe) 170 mg/kg Manganese (Mn) 85 mg/kg
Copper (Cu) 85 mg/kg Zinc (Zn) 30 mg/kg
Boron (B) 45 mg/kg Molybdenum (Mo) 1 mg/kg
100 gram

Planning

e Which fertiliser is best? Plan an investigation to find this out.

9 Variation

9.1 Feet first

Fitting shoes is not easy. People always complain about new shoes and we get the blame! I give good advice but sometimes people have funny-shaped feet – it's not my fault! Some people have feet that are different sizes. One woman came in yesterday with a left foot which was a small size 7 and a right foot was a big size 6. What am I supposed to do? Many people have feet that are wider or narrower than normal ... Have a nice day!

Are Simon's complaints fair? Do people have feet that are different sizes?

You need:
– ruler
– set squares (optional)

Investigating

a Design an investigation to find out how much people's feet vary.
Tackle at least one of the questions below.
● Are a person's feet both the same length?
● Which varies more – the length or the width?
If you can, carry out your investigation.

9.2 Elementary, my dear Watson

Scene:
221B Baker Street, a foggy November evening.
Sherlock HOLMES and Dr WATSON are weighing up their evidence.

WATSON   But will we be defending a murderer, Holmes? Blood on the murder weapon matches our client's blood.

HOLMES   *(Sucking his pipe)* Indeed, but doesn't the letter mention a brother? They could be identical twins.

WATSON   *(Sniffily)* Ah, but they don't look the same. The brother is fat and our client is thin. And the brother has a scar across his right cheek.

HOLMES   I can explain that. It is all quite elementary. You see, twins ... *(A knock on the door. HOLMES opens it.)* Watson! Quickly!

Exeunt

a What was Holmes going to explain to Watson about twins?

b How could the blood on the murder weapon match the client's blood even if the client did not commit the murder?

c The next day, Holmes discovers that his client is a woman. Who must be the murderer? Why?

     KS 3 Assessment Activities Pack A

9.3 Seeds

My seeds are expensive. A packet often has far too many for one sowing. When I've opened a packet, I keep the spare seeds in the fridge to use again later. I don't know if it makes any difference ...

Planning

Does where you store seeds matter?
a Think of some ways you could keep seeds fresher for longer.
b Plan an investigation to find out if your idea was correct. Make sure you explain how your results help you test your original idea.

9.4 Spuds

All potatoes belong to the same species. Its scientific name is *Solanum tuberosum*. But there are many different varieties. Here are some of them:

Variety	Baked	Chipped	Mashed	Roast	Salad	When to Plant	Specialities
Home Guard	☐	☐	◨	☐	☐	E	H
Arran Pilot	☐	☐	◨	☐	☐	E	H, Di
Ulster Sceptre	☐	☐	◨	☐	☐	E	H, Dr
Wilja	◨	◨	■	◨	☐	SE	H, Dr
Desiree	◨	◨	◨	◨	☐	M	H, Di
Maris Piper	■	■	■	◨	☐	M	Di
Pentland Squire	■	■	■	■	☐	M	-
King Edward	■	■	■	■	☐	M	-
Epicure	◨	◨	◨	◨	☐	E	Fr

Uses: ■ = Excellent, ◨ = Good, ☐ = Poor
Season: E = early crop, SE = second early, M = main crop
Specialities: H = high yield, Dr = resists drought,
Di = resists some diseases, Fr = resists frost

a Look at the table and pick the best potatoes for:
– baked potatoes
– chips
– bangers and mash
– growing in cold areas
– a heavy crop
– growing in dry areas

b Plant growers choose the best varieties for their land. They hope everything will go well, but sometimes things don't work out.

Make a list of things that could spoil the growing potatoes.

c You are trying to sell seed potatoes to Farmer Crump from Kent. She wants to buy only one variety of potato in a giant economy pack. This will be cheaper. You try to convince her that three smaller packs of different varieties are better. You tell her that they will give a reasonable crop in any weather conditions.

Write a report for Farmer Crump. You must try to convince her. Your report should include:
– some other reasons for buying more than one variety,
– a recommendation of three varieties to buy. And your reasons.

10 Inheritance

10.1 What are little boys made of?

It is very strange! More male foetuses develop inside the womb than female foetuses. (A foetus is a developing baby.) So there should be more boys around than girls. Good news for the girls? Not quite. Read on ...

Age of foetus	Number of male foetuses that die for every 100 females that die
up to 8 weeks	431
from 9 to 16 weeks	201
from 17 to 42 weeks	134

Country	Number of males born for every 100 females born
UK	106
Cuba	101
USA (Whites)	105
USA (Blacks)	103
Greece	113
South Korea	113

Other information

Boys are more likely to die during childhood than girls. Men tend to die younger than women.

a In which country is a baby most likely to be a boy?

b We think that couples *conceive* about 150 males for every 100 females. Why is the number of males *born* much nearer the number of females *born*?

c The genes in the sperm determine the sex of a foetus. Use diagrams with labels to explain how.

d Why could 'male-carrying' sperms be more successful than 'female-carrying' sperms?

More women than men at 70

10.2 Passing it on?

a Work in a group. Sort the things in the box into three groups:
Group 1 Things that parents pass to a child through the genes.
Group 2 Things that parents do not pass on through the genes.
Group 3 Things you are not sure about.

b Add some more things of your own (at least ten).

c Try to find out more about the items in group 3.

hair colour	being kind to animals
eye colour	having bad dreams as a child
being a fast runner	being good at maths
being very fat	being double-jointed
measles	having a bad temper
length of hair	being able to play a musical instrument
cystic fibrosis	

10.3 Sex tests

In 1967, the organisers of the European Athletics Cup Final, in Kiev, disqualified Ewa Klobukowska for failing a sex test. The test looked at the chromosomes in her cells. The Olympic Committee also took away the gold and bronze medals she had won in the 1964 Olympics.

a Explain how the X- and Y-chromosomes control sex in human beings.

b Ewa had always thought of herself as a woman. Do you think it is fair that the officials forced her to withdraw from the competition? Give your reasons.

© Gott, Price, Thornley/Collins Educational 1992   *KS 3 Assessment Activities Pack A*

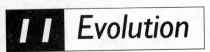

11.1 Pterodactyl families

Pterodactyls probably laid eggs like birds. The baby pterodactyls would
be different from each other and from their parents.

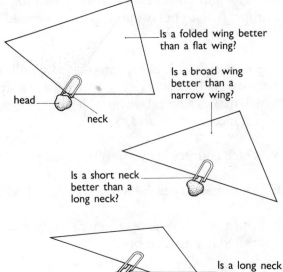

You need:
– cardboard
– paper clips
– Blu-tack
– pair of scissors ⚠

a Make a family of pterodactyls from cardboard,
paper clips and Blu-tack. They should each be different
in some way. For example, some could have a long neck
and others a short neck.

b Test them all to find out which are the best flyers.

c Sort the babies in your pterodactyl family into three groups:
– good flyers,
– average flyers,
– poor flyers.

Pterodactyls were hunters. The best hunters got the most food.
Poor hunters could die from lack of food.

d What do you think could happen to your family of pterodactyls
as they grow? Will they all survive?
● Which will do best? Why?
● Will some branches of the family die out? Why?

e List the adaptations that would make a pterodactyl a good
hunter.

f Why do you think there are no pterodactyls alive today?

11.2 The weaker sex?

A premium is the money you pay once a year to an
insurance company. How much you pay depends on
many things. For example, life assurance premiums
are low for people who are not likely to die young.
If you die and you have paid all your premiums, the
company pays a death benefit to your family.

a Make a list of the things that affect life
assurance premiums.

b Which sorts of people have the lowest premiums?

c Make a list of the reasons you think premiums for
women are lower than for men.

How much you pay every year to get £10 000 if you die

Age	Female		Male	
	Nonsmoker	Smoker	Nonsmoker	Smoker
25	7.40	9.20	13.25	18.20
30	8.85	11.75	17.60	21.45
35	11.15	16.30	20.60	27.90
40	15.10	24.55	26.25	40.25
45	22.55	39.90	37.15	63.05
50	36.10	66.10	57.55	101.60
55	59.75		92.25	
60	98.50		151.90	

12.3 Lead pollution

Read the passage and then answer the questions.

Lead pollution
Lead is a poison which builds up in our bodies over many years. Our bodies store up lead, rather than simply passing it through. So lead pollution is very dangerous.

   Adding lead to petrol is one cause of pollution. When the petrol burns, lead comes out in the exhaust gases. Some people who live near busy roads worry a lot about this.

   Most petrol stations sell unleaded petrol, but not all car engines work properly with it. Most new cars can use unleaded petrol.

   Water pipes are another source of lead pollution. Many years ago, all drinking-water pipes were lead. Some older houses still have lead pipes. Modern houses use copper or plastic pipes instead. Water that passes through lead pipes can dissolve tiny particles of lead which people may drink.

   Lead seems to be a cause of brain damage. It affects babies and young children particularly.

a The passage mentions two main sources of lead pollution. What are they?

b What are the dangers of lead pollution?

c Draw a flow chart to show how lead could get into a young child's body.

d What can be done to reduce lead pollution?

e In a group, produce an eye-catching leaflet or poster about reducing lead pollution.

12.4 The Trans-Alaska pipeline

The Alaskan oilfield is the largest in North America. It provides one-third of the oil and one-eighth of the gas used in the USA. The Trans-Alaska oil pipeline carries hot oil across Alaska from north to south. It forms a barrier to migrating caribou. It crosses snow-covered mountains. Earthquakes and landslips are common there. Heat from the pipes helps to melt the permanently frozen ground.

Here are two newspaper headlines:

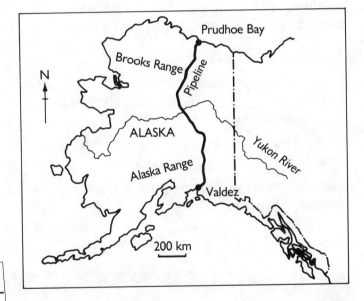

ALASKAN RECORDER

The pipeline – an environmental disaster!

CHICAGO CHRONICLE

Winners and losers in Alaskan oilfield

Investigating

b The pipeline carries hot oil. Why? What effect will temperature have on how well the oil flows? Design an investigation to test your suggestion. Ask your teacher to check it, then carry it out.

a Pick one of the headlines and write a 200 word article to go with it.

c Suggest some ways that the oil in the pipeline could be kept hot.

13 Handling waste

13.1 Can we recycle it?

a Sort the rubbish in the drawings into things that we can recycle and those that we cannot.

b Pick one thing and say how we can recycle it.

c Pick one of the things that we cannot recycle. Explain why we cannot.

d Anything that can be broken down by living things is biodegradable. Which of the things in the drawings are biodegradable?

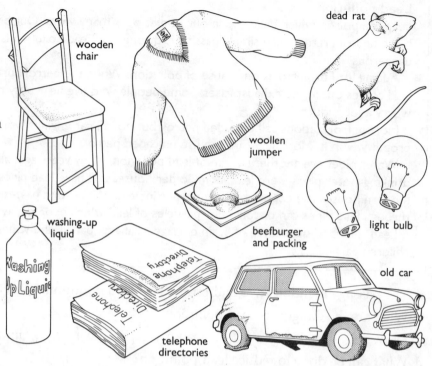

wooden chair

dead rat

woollen jumper

light bulb

washing-up liquid

beefburger and packing

old car

telephone directories

13.2 Water purification

Sterilising tablets will kill harmful bacteria in water. Here is one way of testing for bacteria:

Testing for bacteria

1 Add a measured sample of the water you want to test to some culture solution. Seal the bottle. Culture solution gives the bacteria food to grow.

2 Leave the culture in a warm place for 48 hours. This gives the bacteria time to grow.

3 If there were any bacteria in the original sample, the culture will look cloudy.

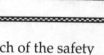

Safety warning
- Only authorised personnel may do this test.
- All equipment used must be sterile.
- All containers must be sealed.
- Liquid waste must be sterilised.
- Solid waste must be burned.

a Explain the need for each of the safety precautions listed.

Planning

b The manufacturer claims that one tablet is enough for one litre of river water. Is this true? Plan an investigation to find out.

c Boiling also kills bacteria. Plan an investigation to see how long a sample of water must be boiled to kill all the bacteria present.

KS 3 Assessment Activities Pack A

13.3 Clean water [AS 1]

Cholera clue in water supply

Doctor John Snow presented his findings at a meeting of the British Medical Association today. His report has already attracted attention, and MPs in the House of Commons are calling on the government to make a statement. The MP for Southwark is particularly concerned about the number of deaths in his constituency.

'I was interested in the number of deaths from cholera in South London.' Doctor Snow explained in his talk. 'Some houses in a street had a whole family suffering from the disease while other houses were completely free of it. I looked at general health and income but I could not find a pattern.

At first, I searched for some hidden factor in the food, but could find none. The people eat food bought from the same shops and markets. They cook in the same way. Their kitchens and sculleries are equally clean. Eventually, the only thing left was the water. This proved to be the breakthrough I was loooking for.

One of two companies supplies most of the houses south of the Thames. The Lambeth Water Company

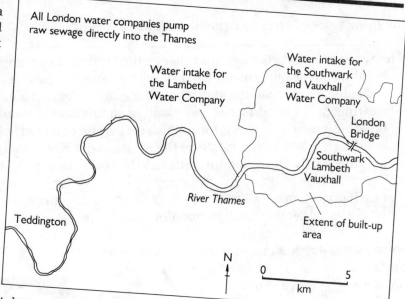

All London water companies pump raw sewage directly into the Thames

takes water from the Thames before the river reaches the city. The Southwark and Vauxhall Water Company have an inlet near London Bridge. Both companies pipe sewage straight into the river. This practice, I feel, is highly dangerous to the health of all.

I have counted the number of deaths from cholera. In 10 000 houses supplied by the Lambeth company, there were 37 deaths in the first seven weeks of the most recent epidemic. The figure for the rest of London (population about 2.5 million) was 59. In the 8000 houses supplied by the Southwark

and Vauxhall company, 315 people died. In one street, houses supplied by Lambeth Water Company were free of cholera. Houses supplied by Southwark and Vauxhall Water Company, in the same street, were infected.'

I insist that the agent which is causing deaths from cholera is entering people's houses through their water supply.

The chairman invited the audience to ask questions and a lively discussion followed. Doctor Snow has supplied a complete set of his figures to the Southwark and Vauxhall Water Company. So far, they have made no comment.

---

a Draw a chart that shows the important figures about cholera deaths and water supplies.

b What pattern can you see in these figures?

c How can you explain this pattern?

Look at *Active Science 1*, pages 34 and 136. Read about cholera and bacteria.

d Snow did not know that bacteria caused cholera. What are bacteria?

e How do cholera bacteria pass from one person to another?

f Untreated sewage still gets into rivers and the sea. Explain why cholera is almost unknown in Britain now.

g When and where do you think there could be a risk of cholera in the modern world? Explain your answer.

14 Local project

14.1 New building

Building work often causes problems for local people.

> Here are some projects that could change the local environment:
> - building a new hypermarket and shopping centre on fields near a ring road,
> - widening an old road through a housing estate as part of a new four-lane ring road,
> - clearing an old building site and planting an urban wildlife park,
> - building a new incinerator for rubbish on the site of an old sewage works,
> - building a new housing estate on the outskirts of town,
> - building a new leisure centre on the site of a derelict, city-centre factory.

a For each project, make a list of the six most important effects it is likely to have. Say whether these will be good or bad effects.

Here are some suggestions. Add more of your own.

more traffic	less traffic
more noise	less noise
more dust	less dust
more shops	fewer shops
more jobs	fewer jobs
houses built	houses knocked down
population rises	population falls
dirtier air	cleaner air
more facilities for local people	fewer facilities for local people

Llanycwmmer

Llanycwmmer is a small town in South Wales. It has a population of 50 000. Many people worked in the coal mining industry, but British Coal is closing the mines. Unemployment is now 17%. Electronics is the basis of much of the new industry in the area. Jobs in these factories are mainly for skilled workers. These workers usually move in from the South of England. This has pushed house prices up.

b Llanycwmmer Council wants to invest in one of the projects listed above. Write a brief report for the council. Advise it about which project would have the best effect on the area. Explain carefully why you chose it instead of the others.

14.2 My patch

Is there a new development planned for your area? It could be new housing, a factory, a road or even planting an avenue of trees or putting up a new bus stop. Look at its effect on the environment.

a Describe the project briefly.

b Make a list of the good effects you expect.

c Make a list of the bad effects you expect.

d Imagine you are one of the people below. Write a letter to the local paper. Say if you are for or against the development. Make it clear who you are:
– a pensioner,
– a 25-year-old insurance company worker with no children,
– a middle-aged parent with three teenage children,
– a homeless 17-year-old.

14.3 The great green giveaway!

> ## £250 000 TO IMPROVE YOUR LOCAL ENVIRONMENT
>
> **Oil UK** is probably the greenest oil company in the world. We were the first petrol company to promote unleaded fuel. We were the first company to use recycled paper for all our office stationery and publications. We were the first company to install high-efficiency fluorescent tubes in all our garages. **Oil UK**'s care for the environment benefits the whole world. And what are you doing for the planet? Buying **Oil UK** fuel helps, but you probably have a pet project that you would like to carry out if only you had the money.
>
> Now you can have can go ahead. **Oil UK** is making available up to £250 000, over the next five years, in grants for local schemes.
>
> Write and tell us how you would like to improve your local environment. If we think it's a good scheme, you could receive a grant of up to £500 towards the cost.
>
> **Oil UK** - a company that cares for the future of the planet!

a Work in small groups. You are going to send a letter to Oil UK to ask for money to improve your local environment. Here are some ideas to get you started:

- Clean up part of the brook.
- Convert a rubbish dump into a wildlife garden.
- Clear the litter near your own school.
- Build a wildlife garden for the local nursery.
- Clean the graffiti from the bus shelter.
- Put up signs to the cycle track.

The flow chart shows you how to write your letter.

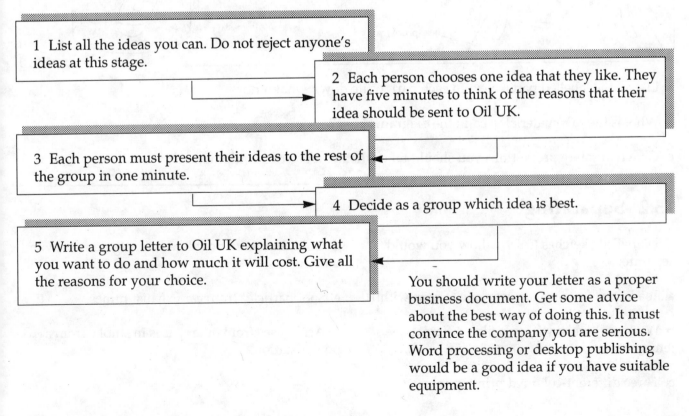

1 List all the ideas you can. Do not reject anyone's ideas at this stage.

2 Each person chooses one idea that they like. They have five minutes to think of the reasons that their idea should be sent to Oil UK.

3 Each person must present their ideas to the rest of the group in one minute.

4 Decide as a group which idea is best.

5 Write a group letter to Oil UK explaining what you want to do and how much it will cost. Give all the reasons for your choice.

You should write your letter as a proper business document. Get some advice about the best way of doing this. It must convince the company you are serious. Word processing or desktop publishing would be a good idea if you have suitable equipment.

15 Getting things

15.1 Distilling

Chemists make perfumes with oils from plants and animals.
For example, they can extract orange oil from orange peel by steam distillation.
The drawing shows the most important parts of steam distillation equipment.

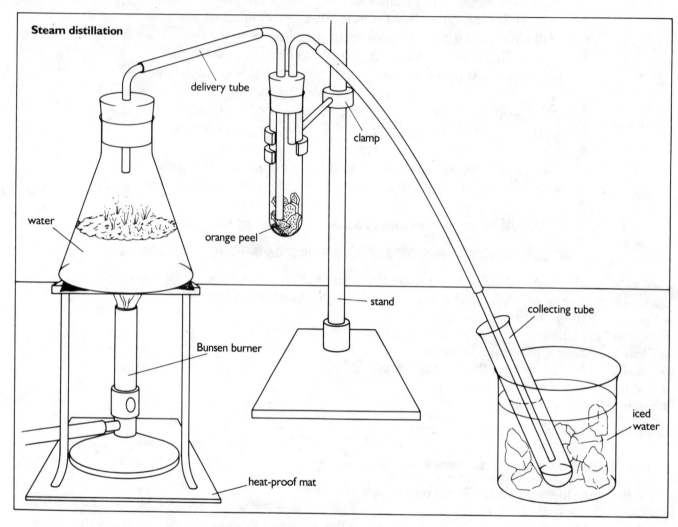

Steam distillation

- delivery tube
- clamp
- water
- orange peel
- stand
- collecting tube
- Bunsen burner
- iced water
- heat-proof mat

a List all the labelled parts. Next to each part, write down what it does.

b What is the raw material used in the diagram above?

c Give two safety precautions you should take when you use this equipment.

15.2 Separating

Use labelled sketches to show how you would separate:

a Tea leaves from tea (an easy one to start with!).

b Water and whisky (they boil at different temperatures).

c Three different-coloured printing inks.

d Gold dust from powdered rock (gold is heavier than rock).

e Soot particles from car exhaust fumes.

f Acid gases from other gases in smoke from a power station.

KS 3 Assessment Activities Pack A

15.3 Fruit juice

The drawing below shows an old-fashioned cider press.
People used it to get juice from apples without letting through
any bits of apple.

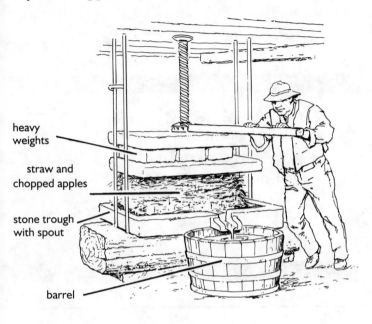

heavy
weights

straw and
chopped apples

stone trough
with spout

barrel

Nineteenth-century cider press

a List all the labelled parts. Next to each
part, write down what it does.

b How would you get rid of any pips that
did get into the juice?

c Design a modern cider press. Label your
design to explain how it works.

d What does the press use as its raw
material?

15.4 Chemistry memory test

Explain the difference between the following pairs
of things. Use diagrams if you can. (*Active Science 3*,
pages 56-63 will help if you get stuck.)

a A mixture (air) and a pure substance (nitrogen).

b An element (oxygen) and a compound (water).

c An atom (O – an oxygen atom) and a molecule
(O_2 – an oxygen molecule).

15.5 ...not a drop to drink

Countries by the sea, that have little water and a
lot of sun, often make drinking water from
seawater. The process is called desalination.

a Why shouldn't you drink seawater?

b Do a sketch with labels to show how you
could make drinking water from seawater.

c Why is 'a lot of sun' important?

15.6 Vacuum cleaner

a There is at least one filter in a vacuum cleaner.
Find out where it is in your cleaner at home.

b Sketch how the cleaner works.

16.1 Getting sorted

You need:
– selection of items from your teacher

Observing

Look at the items in front of you.

a Work with your friends to sort the items into groups based on *what they are made from*. You will all need to agree your classification. Use no more than six groups.

b Agree a title for each group that describes it.

c On your own, write down the name of each group and list its properties.

d Pick three items. Each one must be from a different group. Explain why each item is made of that particular material.

16.2 All wrapped up

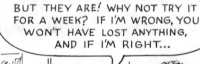

At the head office of Superfry Chip Shops plc, they are arguing about using recycled paper for their chip bags.

a List the things you think are important in deciding what sort of paper to use in a chip shop.

Planning

b Choose two of your ideas and write a plan to test them.

16.3 Spare Parts Inc.

Spare Parts Inc. is a company which does research into spare parts for bodies. Their research scientists have sent a note down to the supply department asking for a delivery. Unfortunately the head scientist has not specified the materials.

a Choose a suitable artificial material for each job.

b Give reasons for each material that you choose.

> **Internal memo**
>
> To: May B Betta, Materials Supply Manager
> From: Frank N Styne, Head Scientist
>
> Please supply suitable materials for:
> – a pin to strengthen a bone
> – a covering for burnt skin
> – a patch for a damaged artery
> – the moving parts for an artificial heart valve

16.4 The right stuff?

This table lists the properties of some common plastics.
You have to use it to choose some plastics for different jobs.

Plastic	Does it burn?	Melting point	Does light pass through it?	Does it conduct heat? 1 = poor 5 = good	How bendy is it?
low-density polythene	yes, little smoke	110 °C	a bit	3	bendy, easily cut
high-density polythene	yes, little smoke	120 °C	a bit	5	fairly stiff, easily cut
PVC	only with difficulty	80 °C	a bit if white	2	bendy
polystyrene	yes, very well	90 °C	a bit if white	1	stiff and hard
nylon	only with difficulty	216 °C	no	3	stiff and hard
Melamine	only with difficulty	does not melt	no	2	stiff and hard
Perspex	yes, easily	does not melt	yes, very well	2	stiff and hard

a Copy the table below, then fill in the blanks.

Job	Plastic I would use	Reasons for my choice
Flask for a child's cold drink		
Ceiling tile to keep heat in		
Windshield for motorbike		
Carton for yoghurt		
Working surface in a kitchen		

Planning

b The numbers for how well something conducts heat (thermal conductivity) are not very accurate. Design a test to give a more accurate way to compare the thermal conductivities of plastics.

17 Describing things

17.1 Acid or alkali?

You need:
- selection of solutions
- indicator paper and colour chart

a Test the chemicals below with an indicator to find out their pH:
- lemon juice
- vinegar
- bleach ⚠
- shampoo
- ammonia solution ⚠
- water

Put your results in a table.

b What do these words mean?
- acid
- alkali
- salt
- neutralisation

17.2 A desirable property?

Fill in the spaces in the table below with at least three examples of suitable materials.
One has been done as an example.

Low-density	High-density
expanded polystyrene	...
loft insulation	...
meringue	...

Soluble	Insoluble
sugar	...
...	...
...	...

Weak	Strong
...	...
...	...
...	...

17.3 Norma the Forger

Beware! Norma the Forger is on the loose!

The police confirmed earlier today that a forger may be at work in our area. 'She specialises in £5 notes', explained Inspector Keynes of the Fraud Squad, 'She has developed a perfect match for the blue ink the Mint uses to print the notes. The public should be on their guard. The notes in their wallets could be worthless if Norma is up to her tricks. Look out for notes that don't have a watermark on the paper. That's a sure sign of a counterfeit. The only other way to check the notes is to use a chromatographic technique to test the ink. The Mint uses only one pure ink, but Norma has to use a mixture to get the right colour.'

a Your teacher has supplied you with ink samples. One of them is Norma's counterfeit mixture. The other is the pure colour used by the Royal Mint. Test them to find out which is which.

b Write a sentence to explain the difference between a mixture and a compound.

© Gott, Price, Thornley/Collins Educational 1992   *KS 3 Assessment Activities Pack A*

17.4 What happens next?

You need:
– selection of metals
– copper (II) sulphate solution (1 M)
– sodium chloride solution (1 M)

a Make predictions of what will happen in the experiments below. Remember: nothing might happen! Explain the reasons for your predictions.

● Put a piece of clean magnesium into water.
● Put a piece of zinc into a solution of copper sulphate.
● Put a piece of copper into water.
● Put a piece of zinc into a solution of sodium chloride.

b Now do the tests to see if you were right. If not, write down what did happen and explain why.

c Your teacher will put a piece of sodium into water. What do you expect to happen? Why?

17.5 Mystery elements

The data on elements and the Periodic Table on pages 56–61 of *Active Science 3* will help you to answer these questions.

a Work in pairs. One of you should pick an element. The other person can ask up to ten questions to find out what element it is. You can only answer 'Yes' or 'No'. You score a point for every question your partner asks.

b Swap over and try again. The first person to 30 points is the winner.

c Which sorts of question are most useful?

d Try to develop a system of questions that identify the element as quickly as possible.

17.6 Elementary groups

You need
– selection of elements

a Look at the chemicals you have been given. Sort them into groups. Explain why you have chosen those groups.

b Compare your groups with those of other people. Try to work out a system that everyone agrees with.

c In which of your groups would you put the following elements?

– **Bromine** is a dark red liquid which gives off a poisonous vapour at room temperature. Potassium explodes in bromine gas. Liquid bromine does not conduct electricity.

– **Silicon** can be a silvery solid or a dull grey powder. It conducts electricity, but not as well as conductors like iron and copper. It is called a semiconductor. It does not react with water. Sand is mostly silicon dioxide: a hard, solid oxide of silicon.

– **Radium** is a metal that was first isolated by Marie Curie. Radium is radioactive and can cause cancer. Radium atoms break down to give out a radioactive gas called radon. Radon reacts with air to give a basic oxide.

18 Solids, liquids and gases

18.1 Joe's snowman

Use the idea of particles to explain to Joe what has happened to his snowman.

18.2 In a state

Look at the diagram below.

a Explain carefully what each of the words in the circles means.

b 'My gran knows about jellies! She says that if you want to get a jelly out of a mould, you should stand the mould in hot water for a few seconds. When you turn the mould upside down the jelly will drop out. I always use a knife to get the jelly out and I end up cutting off the rabbit's ears!'

Why does the warmth help to get the jelly out? Use some of the words from the diagram to help you explain.

c 'My mum wants a new fridge. The seal round the door is broken and this lets the air into the fridge. The freezer box gets covered in ice and we have to defrost it nearly every week!'

The ice comes from water vapour in the air. Why does it collect on the freezer compartment? Use some of the words from the diagram to help you explain.

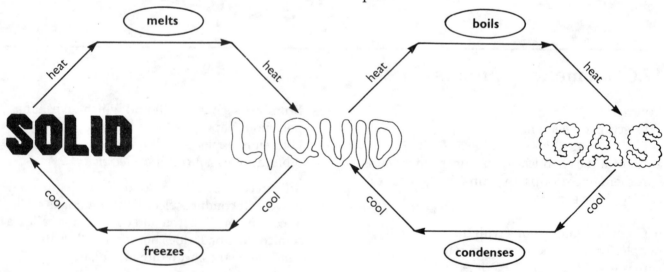

18.3 Can you take the pressure?

Your teacher will heat a can containing a very small amount of water until steam comes out of the top. Then your teacher will screw the lid on tightly and stop heating the can.

a Write down what you think will happen. Explain why you think this.

Now watch your teacher do the experiment.

b Were you right? If not, write down what really happened and why.

18.4 Buying gas

It is easy to measure how much you have of a solid or a liquid. Look at the items in the picture and answer the questions:

a What units do we use to measure amounts of solids? Can you find any exceptions? If so, which ones?

b What units do we use to measure amounts of liquids? Can you find any exceptions? If so, which ones?

Amounts of gases are more difficult to measure.

c How is the camping gas sold?

d Why is butane gas not sold by volume?

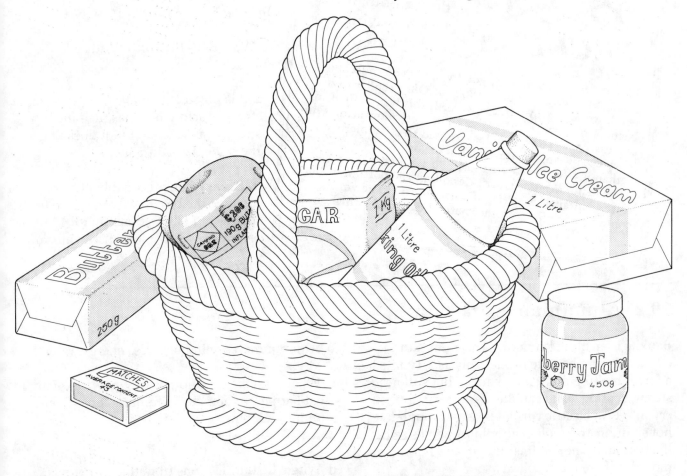

You are going with your friends on a three-day camping expedition. You need to know how much gas to take with you. You cannot afford to waste a whole can to find out how long one can lasts.

e Plan an investigation to find out how many cans to take with you.

18.5 Balls and balloons

'My mum says you have to warm up a squash ball before you start to play. If you don't, the ball won't bounce properly.'

'What happens if you take a balloon out of a warm room into a very cold place? I reckon it will get smaller, but my brother says I'm wrong.'

a Work in a group to discuss each of these statements. What is going on in each case?

b Then, on your own, write down what you think is happening. Make sure you explain why you think that.

19.1 Posset's vinegar

> ### Posset's OLD PECULIAR
> is the best beer in the world. So why do we pour it over beech shavings to make it go off?
>
> The reason is, if you want good vinegar you must start with good beer. We pour gallons of Old Peculiar over beech wood shavings in a tower. All this beer is food for bacteria that convert the ethanol into ethanoic acid. Our scientists say 'The ethanol is oxidised to ethanoic acid'. They even write out the reaction for us:
>
> ethanol + oxygen → ethanoic acid + water
>
> The malt vinegar that trickles out at the bottom of the tower contains about 4% of ethanoic acid. The vinegar contains a mixture of other natural chemicals which make Posset's Vinegar taste so good.

a What is the chemical name for the acid found in vinegar?

b Why are wood shavings used in the tower?

c What does the word 'oxidised' mean?

d It is possible to make a 4% solution of ethanoic acid which has the same strength as vinegar. But it doesn't taste the same. Explain why.

e Some vinegar is distilled to remove the brown colour. Draw and label a diagram to show how you could distil vinegar.

19.2 Aluminium extraction

Bauxite is an aluminium ore. The aluminium is extracted from bauxite by electrolysis. Cryolite has a lower melting point than bauxite but still needs strong heating. (The bauxite dissolves in molten cryolite.) An electric current passes through the hot solution and molten aluminum settles out at the bottom of the cell. It is run off, as a liquid, into moulds where it can solidify.

a Aluminum extraction uses very large amounts of energy. Give two reasons for this.

b Aluminium recycling uses less energy. Why?

c What does the equation below show? Explain what happens when the aluminium ions change to aluminium atoms.
$$Al^{3+} + 3e^- \rightarrow Al$$

d Where do the electrons from this reaction go?
$$2O^{2-} \rightarrow O_2 + 4e^-$$

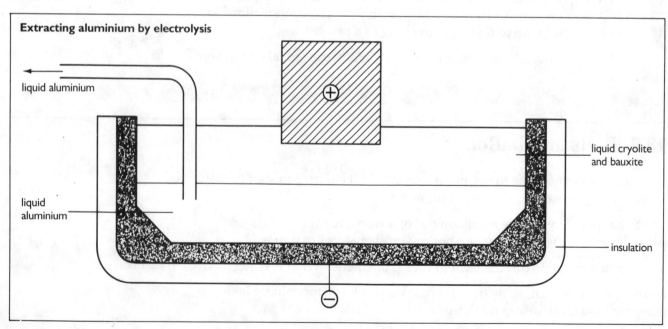

Extracting aluminium by electrolysis

liquid aluminium

liquid aluminium

liquid cryolite and bauxite

insulation

KS 3 Assessment Activities Pack A

19.3 Copper

Copper was one of the first metals used by humans. This is because it is quite easy to extract from its ore. Two methods can be used.

1 Reduction with carbon

Heat powdered copper ore in a crucible with carbon. The copper ore is reduced. The equation is:

copper oxide + carbon → copper + carbon dioxide

2 Electrolysis

Warm copper ore in dilute sulphuric acid to dissolve it. This makes copper sulphate:

copper oxide + sulphuric acid → copper sulphate + water

Then filter the mixture. Pass an electric current through the blue solution. Copper will coat one of the electrodes.

a You have to use energy to get copper from its ore. How do you know that both methods need energy?

b What does 'reduced' mean in method 1?

c What waste products would you have to get rid of with method 1?

d Draw a set of sketches that show each stage of method 2. Label your sketches.

e People made copper from its ore over 4000 years ago. Which method do you think they used then? Why?

Planning

f Plan an investigation to find out which method produces more copper from a sample of ore.

19.4 Raw and manufactured materials

a The list below includes seven raw materials and seven materials that are manufactured from them. Set out the two types and pair them up in a table like that on the right.

oil	air
table salt	galena
paper	polythene
seawater	steel
wool	fleece
iron ore	lead
pine trees	dry ice

Raw material	Manufactured material
pine trees	paper

b Add another five pairs of materials to the table.

20.1 Coffee

Potboiler Inc. make instant coffee. They are the market leaders
because they spend so much money on research and development.
Their top scientist, Samantha B. Kerr, is discussing her latest plan
with the managing director, Munn E. Baggs.

Planning

a Samantha asks you to organise the testing.
Make a plan for an investigation to answer this question:

● Will grinding the beans into a finer powder let the flavour
out into the water more quickly?

You may be able to carry out part of your plan. If you can, use
your results to write the report for Munn E. Baggs.

KS 3 Assessment Activities Pack A

20.2 All washed up

You need:
– samples of washing-up liquid

Your teacher has watered down some washing-up liquid. The four test bottles are:

Bottle no.	Percentage washing-up liquid	Percentage water
1	100	0
2	75	25
3	50	50
4	25	75

Investigating

a Design and carry out a test to find out how the amount of water affects the strength of the washing-up liquid. Write a report for the Trading Standards inspector.

b Hilda said the Trading Standards tests were no good because they used cold water. She said people wash up in hot water and her washing-up liquid works well at the right temperature. Plan an investigation to find out how temperature affects the results of your test. Is Hilda right?

20.3 Greener cars

A catalyst alters the speed of a chemical reaction. Some cars use a catalyst to clean up the exhaust gases. A catalytic converter uses a catalyst made from rare metals. The exhaust from the engine passes over the catalyst and harmful gases react to form safer gases.

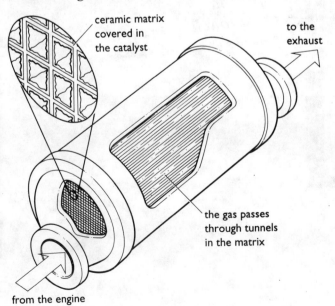

ceramic matrix covered in the catalyst

to the exhaust

the gas passes through tunnels in the matrix

from the engine

The following reactions take place in a catalytic converter in a car exhaust system:

unburnt petrol → water + carbon dioxide

nitrogen oxides → nitrogen + oxygen

carbon monoxide → carbon dioxide

The reaction does not change the catalyst. The catalyst helps the reaction unless it gets 'poisoned' by impurities. Lead in petrol will 'poison' the catalyst in a car. So cars with catalytic converters must use unleaded petrol.

a Explain, in your own words, what a catalyst is.

b What gases would you find coming from a normal exhaust?

c What gases would you find coming from the exhaust of a car fitted with a catalytic converter?

d Why are only a few cars fitted with catalytic converters?

e Why do the exhaust gases go through a lot of fine tubes in a catalytic converter?

21.1 Electrolysis

Your teacher is going to pass electricity through some chemicals.
Observe what happens very carefully. Draw the table below and fill it in.

Substance	Does electricity flow through		
	cold solid?	molten solid?	solution?

a Write down any patterns you can see in your results.

b Suggest an explanation for the patterns.

c Explain what you can see happening in these experiments.

21.2 Shower soap dish

The Noah Bathroom Company makes the shell soap dish.
It is Noah's first product in a cut-throat market and the
company is keen to get it right. They have a choice of at
least four different materials to make the dish. Their
designers have suggested plastic, steel, aluminium
and brass.

'Noah bathroom fittings

– for that extra touch of luxury.'

a Make a list of the advantages and disadvantages of
each material.

Noah's designers have chosen steel because it is cheap
and strong. However, there is one problem – it rusts.
To deal with this, Noah will coat the dish with a
rust-proofing paint.

Planning

b Design an investigation to find out:
– which type of paint is best,
– how thick the coating of paint needs to be.

Remember: you must make your test as much
like the conditions in a shower as possible.

c Make a list of other ways to prevent rusting.

© Gott, Price, Thornley/Collins Educational 1992 *KS 3 Assessment Activities Pack A*

21.3 Electrochemistry memory test

What do these words mean:

a anode?   b cathode?   c solvent?   d solution?   e electrolysis?

21.4 Rotten with rust

Study the table below from a *Which?* survey done in 1990 and answer questions **a** to **c**.

a Pick the two cars that you think are best at resisting rust.

b Pick two cars that you think are worst at resisting rust.

c How will the rust affect the safety and value of the cars?

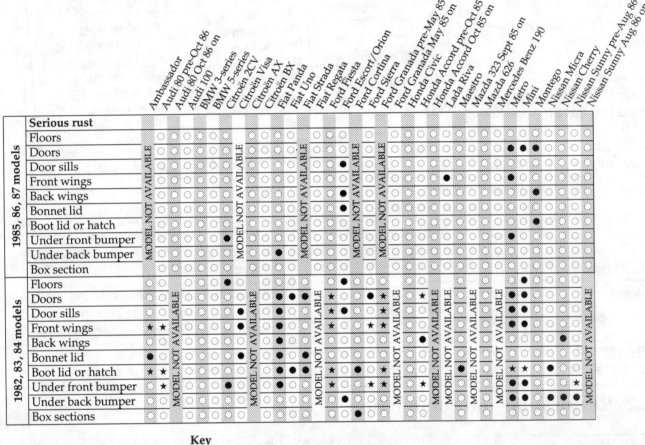

Key

★ = better than average   ○ = average   ● = worse than average

The table on the right shows differences between a rust survey carried out in 1985 and the one in 1990.

d Which part of cars shows:
– the largest improvement?
– the smallest improvement?

e Prepare a suitable chart for an advertisement. The chart should show how much better cars resisted rust in 1990 than they did in 1985.

f How can we prevent rust damage to cars?

Rust 1985 to 1990

PART	Six-year old cars in 1985 %	Six-year old cars in 1990 %
Floors	2	less than 1
Doors	11	5
Door sills	9	4
Front wings	13	3
Back wings	5	2
Bonnet lid	5	2
Bootlid or hatch	9	5
Roof	1	1
Under front bumper	4	3
Under back bumper	3	1
Box sections	1	less than 1
Jacking points	2	less than 1

22 Oxidation

22.1 Putting out fires

Use the tables below to help you answer these questions:

a What class of fire is a chip-pan fire?

b What types of extinguisher could you use?

c What did Mrs Ferno do wrong?

d What types of fire extinguisher equipment should you have in a kitchen? Explain your choice.

THEY'VE HAD THEIR CHIPS!

Mrs Irma Ferno was under sedation yesterday following her rescue from the fire that destroyed New Clapham House. The fire started in Mrs Ferno's second-floor flat. Mrs Ferno was cooking chips when the oil in the chip pan caught fire. She tried to douse the fire with water, but the blaze quickly spread throughout the building.

The flats were the subject of much controversy when they were built three years ago. 'Clapham Likes Aged Property Preserved' (CLAPP), the protest group, has been trying to have the building condemned ever since.

Yesterday, Mrs Ferno's accident did the job for them. Mrs Ferno's daughter Ann denied rumours that CLAPP had made any payments into her mother's post office account. 'She's just not a very good cook.'

Class of fire	Examples	Choice of extinguisher
Class A	ordinary combustibles, e.g. wood, paper, cloth, rubber, plastics	water
Class B	flammable liquid fires, e.g. cooking fat, oil, paraffin, petrol, methylated spirits	fire blanket, carbon dioxide extinguisher, foam extinguisher, powder extinguisher (Never use water.)
Class C	electrical fires	carbon dioxide (Never use water or foam, and always switch off the electricity supply before you tackle the fire.)
Class D	metal fires, e.g. sodium, magnesium	dry powder

22.2 Respiration and combustion

Respiration

Respiration uses up sugar and oxygen and gives out water and carbon dioxide. The energy stored in the sugar is released and can be used by the body. All this happens at the normal body temperature – just below 37° C. Respiration happens in every living cell in the body.

Combustion

Combustion is the chemical reaction we normally call burning. It uses up a fuel and oxygen. It gives out different things depending on the fuel used. Mains gas is methane. When this burns, it gives out water and carbon dioxide. Some plastics give out poisonous fumes when they burn. Suffocation and poisoning, on their own, kill many people in fires.

a Describe two ways that combustion and respiration are similar.

b Describe two ways that combustion and respiration are different.

c Here are three true statements. They seem a bit confusing:

- You can help a glowing piece of wood to burn by blowing on it gently.
- The air we breathe out contains more carbon dioxide than normal air.
- Carbon dioxide puts out flames.

Explain carefully why blowing on a piece of wood helps it to burn.

22.3 Burning fabrics

Investigating

a Jotinda has asked you to test some fabric samples. Plan an investigation to find out which of the fabric samples you have been given are flame resistant. You will not be able to use a lighted cigarette. What else would do? It is no good using a Bunsen burner - you don't find many of them in normal living rooms!

You need:
– fabric samples

b What safety precautions will you use in your investigation?

c Once your teacher has checked your plan, carry it out. You must use small amounts of material. Think safe!

My name is Jotinda and I work for Supersofa Furniture. My job is to find out which fabrics and foams are safest in a fire. We test small amounts of fabrics with a lighted cigarette to see if they will burst into flame. Fabrics have to be able to survive a lighted cigarette before they can be used on furniture.

d When you have finished, write a report for Jotinda. In your report:

● List the fabrics samples in order, with the one that burns most easily first.
● Say which fabrics are safe to use on furniture.

e Find out what materials are used in each fabric (e.g. cotton, polyester). Does this help to explain your findings?

22.4 Discovering oxygen

Look at the passage about Priestley's work on 'airs' in *Active Science 1* on page 60.

a Which gas was once called 'inflammable air'?

b What did Priestley do to provide heat for his experiment?

c What experiments did Priestley do that told him the gas he had produced was different from air?

d Who do you think discovered oxygen? Was it Priestley or Lavoisier? Say how you decided.

Antoine Lavoisier's wife, Marie, was his most trusted helper. She worked with him to produce the book *Traité de chimie*. After he was guillotined, she completed another book, *Memoire de chimie*, on her own. This book gave more details about the Lavoisiers' experiments and ideas.

e Imagine you are Marie Lavoisier. Write a letter to Joseph Priestley explaining what happened to your husband. Say how you feel about continuing with the research.

22.5 Reactions and energy

Most chemical reactions give out or take in energy. For example, burning coal gives out heat and light when it reacts with oxygen in the air.

a List at least five more reactions that give out or take in energy and say how the energy is transferred.

23 Particles

23.1 Dissolving

If you put a sweet into water, it disappears slowly.

a Explain the difference between 'melting' and 'dissolving'. Give an example of each process.

b Write down three things that should make the sweet dissolve faster.

c Tiny particles make up the sweet ... and everything else. Explain, using the particle model, how each of your answers to **b** helps the sweet to dissolve.

Planning

d Pick one of your answers to **b** and write a plan to investigate your idea.

23.2 Collapsing and exploding

These words might be useful when you answer the questions below:
– pressure
– air
– particles
– spread out

Aerosol air-fresheners contain a mixture of gas and perfume. When you press the button, the gas squirts out. It carries some of the perfume with it.

a Why does the gas squirt out if you press the button?

b After a few minutes, you can smell the perfume in the hall, even if you sprayed in the living room. Explain how the smell gets to the hall.

c Pressurisation keeps the air in an aircraft cabin at a pressure which is higher than the air at 10 000 metres up, but lower than the pressure on the ground. As the aircraft climbs or comes down, passengers may notice their ears 'popping'. Can you explain why?

d Why are aerosol cans banned on aeroplanes?

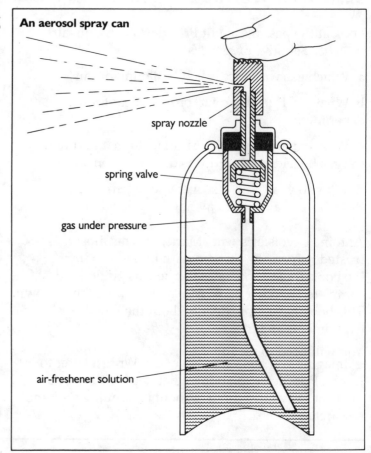

An aerosol spray can

spray nozzle

spring valve

gas under pressure

air-freshener solution

e Submarines often have their air at a higher pressure than the surface air pressure. What might happen to aerosol cans in deep-sea submarines?

  © Gott, Price, Thornley/Collins Educational 1992   *KS 3 Assessment Activities Pack A*

23.3 Koolies

Koolies are pads of material with a perfumed liquid on them. You wipe them on your face and hands. The liquid evaporates and you feel fresher.

a What does the word 'evaporate' mean?

b Why do Koolies cool you down?

Planning

You have to test some liquids to find out which could be used in Koolies. Plan an investigation to answer one of the questions below. For safety reasons, you cannot use your skin for testing.

c Which liquid gives the best cooling effect?

d Which liquid, and how much of it, would you use for a Koolie? Explain your answer.

23.4 Window blow-out

a Explain what forced Captain Trubs out of the cabin when the window glass broke. Use the words 'particles' and 'pressure' in your answer.

Captain Heidi Trubs was nearly sucked out of her aeroplane yesterday when the glass of the cockpit window blew out.

'The first thing I knew' Captain Trubs explained later, 'I was hanging out of the plane 30 000 feet above Lancashire. I must have blacked out then.'

Nigel Macnaff, the co-pilot, grabbed his captain's legs and pulled her back into the de-pressurised cabin. The runways at Manchester were cleared for an emergency landing and within 15 minutes Macnaff had the aircraft back on the ground. None of the passengers was injured.

23.5 Printer's mistake!

Look carefully at the diagram. It is from a science textbook for 13-year-old students. The diagram is part of a section describing the differences between solids, liquids and gases. Unfortunately, the printer has lost the text and the book must be ready in two days' time!

You have to write some new text. Your text must show how scientists explain the differences between solids, liquids and gases using the idea of atoms.

You will need to mention:
– how close together the atoms are,
– how fast they are moving.

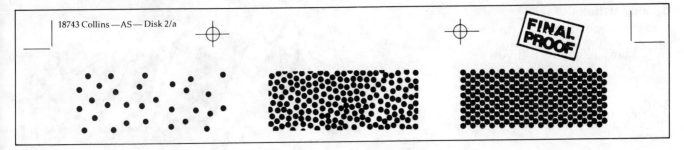

18743 Collins —AS— Disk 2/a

FINAL PROOF

24 Reactions

24.1 Describing reactions

Here are some different types of chemical reaction:
A Fermentation
B Combustion (burning)
C Respiration
D Photosynthesis
E Adding oxygen (an example of oxidation)
F Taking away oxygen (an example of reduction)
G Acid/carbonate
H Acid/base

Make up as many reactions of each type as you can, using the chemicals in the table. Reactants are the chemicals that react. Products are the chemicals that the reaction makes.

Reactants	Products
carbon dioxide	hydrogen
water	sugar
carbon	carbon
hydrogen	water
ethanol	carbon dioxide
sugar	iron
calcium carbonate	ethanol
hydrochloric acid	methane
oxygen	sodium chloride
iron oxide	hydrochloric acid
sodium hydroxide	calcium chloride
methane	oxygen

You can use two reactants, if you want, and you may get several products. One has been done for you to get you started:

A Fermentation
   sugar → carbon dioxide + ethanol

And here is the start of another:

B Combustion
   carbon + oxygen →

How many reactions did you get?
1–3   plenty more to find
4–6   not too bad
7–10   good
more than 10   brilliant

KS 3 Assessment Activities Pack A

24.2 To react or not?

a baking a cake

This is an extract from a science text book:

A chemical reaction takes place when atoms and molecules re-arrange themselves. You can recognise a chemical reaction because some of these things happen:
– the chemicals look different afterwards,
– it is hard to get the starting chemicals back,
– the chemicals get hot or cold.

Which things on this page are chemical reactions? Explain your answers.

b washing your hair

c using a gas fire

d using an electric fire

e making a cup of tea

f opening a bottle of fizzy drink

g watercolour paint drying

KS 3 Assessment Activities Pack A

25 Atoms and molecules

25.1 Symbols

Hundreds of years ago, alchemists used these symbols for different chemicals.

a Why don't modern chemists use these symbols?

b What symbols do modern chemists use for:
– carbon
– oxygen
– hydrogen
– gold
– sulphur
– lead?

air	gypsum	phosphorus
antimony	iron	quicklime
arsenic	lead	sulphuric acid
common salt	lime	urine
copper	mercury	vinegar
earth	nickel	water
fire		
gold	nitrous acid	zinc

Some of the chemical symbols used by alchemists

25.2 Molecular model-making

You need:
– modelling clay
– cocktail sticks

Build a model of one molecule of each of these substances:
a water (H_2O)
b sulphur dioxide (SO_2)
c methane (CH_4)
d carbon dioxide (CO_2)
e hydrogen (H_2)
f ammonia (NH_3)
g ethane (C_2H_6)
h ozone (O_3) – a hard one!

25.3 Molecular shapes

Look at the drawings of molecule models on page 13 in *Active Science 3*.

a Describe how the atoms of lead and sulphur are arranged in the first drawing.

b Describe the arrangement of oxygen atoms in the first drawing.

c Describe two differences between the arrangement of atoms in lead sulphide (drawing 1) and the arrangement of atoms in carbon dioxide (drawing 4).

25.4 Molecular memory test

Write down the meanings of these words:
a atom
b ion
c molecule
d element
e compound

26 Radiation

26.1 X-ray doses

Radiographers and dentists use X-rays to look inside our bodies. The X-ray pictures give useful information to doctors and have helped to save many lives. In 1990 *Which?* magazine did a survey of 502 people in Britain who had been X-rayed.

The most common X-rays and how much radiation they need

Type of X-rays	Percentage of all X-ray examinations	Average dose (units of radiation)	Time to get same dose from natural radiation
dental	25	20	3 days
limbs and joints	25	100	16 days
chest	24	50	8 days
spine (lower)	7	2200	1 year
spine (higher)		900	5 months
skull	5.6	200	1 month
stomach and intestines (barium meal)	2.5	3800	1.7 years
stomach and intestines (barium enema)		7700	3.5 years
abdomen	2.9	1400	8 months
pelvis	2.9	1200	7 months
urinary system	1.3	4400	2 years

a How many people in the survey had had a dental X-ray?

b Which X-ray examination uses the smallest dose?

c How long does it take to receive the same dose from the natural background radiation as from one skull X-ray?

d Which three types of X-ray make up almost three-quarters of the total?

X-ray dangers

X-rays can damage cells in the body. Sometimes this makes the cell start to grow out of control. This can lead to cancer. The National Radiological Protection Board estimates that, every year in Britain, between 100 and 250 people die from cancers caused by X-rays. There are 160 000 cancer deaths every year in Britain. X-rays can also cause changes to the reproductive cells. These changes could lead to damaged babies many years later.

X-ray precautions

- Before taking an X-ray photograph, the radiologist should ask if you have had an X-ray recently. This is to avoid doing the same X-ray twice unless it is essential.
- The radiologist should protect your testes or ovaries with a lead shield.
- If you are female, the radiologist should ask you if you could be pregnant.
- When you change your dentist, your old dentist should send your dental X-rays to the new dentist.

---

e An X-ray of the urinary system gives a large dose. Give two reasons why this particular type of X-ray could be dangerous.

f Design a poster for a hospital waiting room. It should explain why doctors use X-rays and warn people about the dangers of radiation. It must not be too frightening. The poster should tell them how to reduce any risks.

27 Weather

27.1 Weather maps

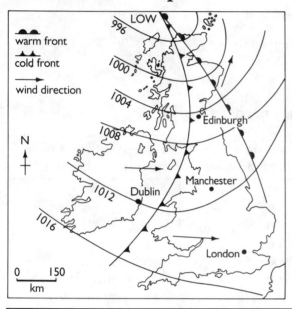

a What is the wind direction in Manchester?

b What is the wind direction in Dublin?

c Sketch the map on your paper and:
- Use blue to colour the coldest areas on your map.
- Use red to colour the warmest areas on your map.

d Is the air over the British Isles usually moist or dry?

e Will England and Wales become warmer or cooler as the fronts move towards the east?

f Where does cold, dry air over Britain usually come from?

g 'Air from the Atlantic always brings rain.' Is this true? Explain why.

27.2 Predicting weather changes

Seaweed gets damp if its going to rain.

Red sky at night, shepherds delight;
Red in the morning, shepherds warning.

If fir cones open up the weather is going to get warmer.

If it rains on St Swithin's Day it will rain for 40 days afterwards.

Planning

a Plan an investigation to test one of the sayings above. Make sure you explain:
- what evidence you will collect,
- how you will collect it,
- how you will interpret your evidence.

b Design equipment you could use to measure the important things about the weather in your area.

27.3 Water in the air

Claire looks after the school glasshouse. She told us:

'I watered the plants in the glasshouse yesterday, when the Sun was out, and it soon got very hot and sticky in there. When I went in this morning, it was much cooler and all the glass had misted up. Water was running down the panes of glass and dripping from the aluminium frame.'

a Explain what was happening. Use the words below in your explanation:
- evaporation
- condensation
- vapour
- liquid
- humid
- temperature.

b The same things happen in the open air to give rain clouds and downpours. Explain how energy from the sun can make this happen.

27.4 Climate and vegetation

South America: countries

South America: vegetation types

South America: summer rainfall (cm)

South America: summer temperatures (°C)

Study the maps of South America.

a What is the summer rainfall in Venezuela?

b Which country has the highest summer temperature?

c Where are the main areas of desert?

d What sorts of vegetation would you expect to find in Colombia?

e Why are there no rainforests in Chile? Use the maps showing rainfall and summer temperatures to help you.

f How would a drought in Argentina affect the cattle ranchers?

KS 3 Assessment Activities Pack A

28 The Earth's surface

28.1 Disaster!

The table lists some of the worst natural disasters in the last 500 years.

Disaster	Where it happened	Date	Number killed
worst volcanic eruption	Krakatoa, Indonesia	1883	36 000
worst earthquake	Shensi, China	1556	830 000
worst flood	Hwang-ho river, China	1931	3 700 000
worst landslide	Kansu province, China	1556	200 000
worst avalanche	Huaras, Peru	1941	about 5000
worst hurricane	Ganges Delta, Bangladesh	1970	1 000 000

a 'Hurricanes are much more dangerous than earthquakes.'
Do you think this is true? Give reasons for your answer.

b Explain why some disasters cause more deaths than others.

c Choose two of the natural disasters. Explain why they happen.

28.2 Soils

Here is some information from a gardening book about different sorts of soils.

Soil type	Appearance	Physical qualities	Chemical qualities
Clay soil	Soil is covered by water in wet weather. Sedges, rushes, buttercup, alder, willow in evidence.	Very slow to drain. Sticky, greasy if wet; hard and lumpy when dry.	Rich in plant food. Frequently neutral.
Medium loam	Strong-growing roses, shrubs and grasses.	Drains moderately quickly. Easy to dig over.	Usually well supplied with plant food.
Light loam	Intermediate between medium and sandy soil.		
Sandy soil	Light coloured soil. Gorse, broom and Scots pine. Heather in acid sands.	Quick draining. Easily worked in moist conditions. Gritty to the touch.	Low level of nutrients. Often very acid. Needs fertiliser.
Chalky or limestone soil	White or whitish subsoil. Dogwood, viburnum and clematis grow well.	Chalk is pasty when moist. Limestone is gritty to the touch.	Low in organic matter. Alkaline.
Peaty soil	Dark, fibrous soil. Alder and willow trees often present	Spongy and fibrous.	Low in phosphates. Often acid.
Stony soil	Often light-coloured. Many stones on surface. Sparse vegetation.	Shallow soil with many rocks and stones.	Low nutrient content. Needs a lot of fertiliser.

a Which soil is often very acid?

b If you put each of these soils in a glass funnel and add water to the top, which soil will let the water through most *slowly*?

c Which soil is most likely to form on top of limestone rock? Why?

d Which soil is most likely to form on sandstone rock? Why?

e Explain how limestone soil is made from rocks.

    © Gott, Price, Thornley/Collins Educational 1992   KS 3 Assessment Activities Pack A

28.3 Loch Oich

The drawing shows Loch Oich in Scotland. Loch Ness can just be seen in the background. After the formation of the rocks in Scotland, the Great Glen fault split the country in two. This fault is large enough to be seen clearly on a map of Scotland. In the past, a large glacier filled the fault, and eroded it to make a steep-sided valley. As the Earth warmed up, rocks and grit, left by the melting glacier, blocked the valley. Rivers flowing into it made the deep lochs (lakes).

a Draw a series of sketches that show the stages in the formation of Loch Oich.

b Why was erosion greatest along the fault line?

c The lochs are filling up with sediment now. Where does the sediment come from?

d What will the valley look like in a few thousand years?

e How will the local people know if the fault moves again?

Great Glen fault

28.4 Rocks and minerals

Observing

a Do some tests on your rocks:
● Look carefully at their grains with a hand lens.
● Rub them together.
● Drop them.
● Scratch them.
Take care not to damage the room or yourself.

b Look at your results and decide which rock would be best for:
– a shop front,
– a road surface,
– chippings for concrete,
– carving into a statue.
Give reasons for your choices.

You need:
– hand lens
– sharp object (a compass point or nail would do ⚠)
– rocks and a mineral

c Write a description of each rock for a stonemason's catalogue. The description should include the important features of the rock and a list of the things it can be used for.

d Look carefully at the mineral. What differences can you see between the mineral and the rocks?

e Both minerals and rocks come from the Earth's crust. What is special about a mineral?

29 Inside the Earth

29.1 The rock cycle AS 3

a Pair up the words below with the statements about rocks:

1 burial	A Rocks are broken into smaller rocks by water, wind or changes in temperature.
2 cementing	B Natural forces move broken rock pieces, made by weathering, to new places.
3 deposition	C A river moves pieces of rock.
4 erosion	D Sediments form in layers, usually under water.
5 eruption	E Sediments pile up making more and more layers.
6 heating and squeezing	F The sediments are stuck together to make a layer of rock.
7 melting	G Rocks change into different forms because of high temperature and pressure.
8 transport	H Solid rocks are melted by great heat to form magma.
9 weathering	I Molten rock is pushed out from volcano as lava.

b On page 25 of *Active Science 3*, there is a drawing of the rock cycle.
Make a similar cycle, using your pairs of words and statements.
Read the book first, then try to do the activity without using it.
Check your final version with the book.

29.2 Journey to the centre of the Earth

In 1864, Jules Verne published a science-fiction novel called
Journey to the centre of the Earth. In the story, three explorers walk to the
centre of the Earth. They travel along a passage leading from an extinct
volcano in Iceland.

We now know this journey is impossible.

a Describe briefly how we have changed our view of the
Earth's interior since 1864.

© Gott, Price, Thornley/Collins Educational 1992   *KS 3 Assessment Activities Pack A*

29.3 Volcanoes and earthquakes

a Yellowstone National Park in Wyoming, USA, is famous for its mountain scenery and for the geysers of boiling water and steam. It is in a region that has earthquakes, and there are several volcanic areas nearby. Write a brochure for the Park. It should explain why there are so many tourist attractions close together.

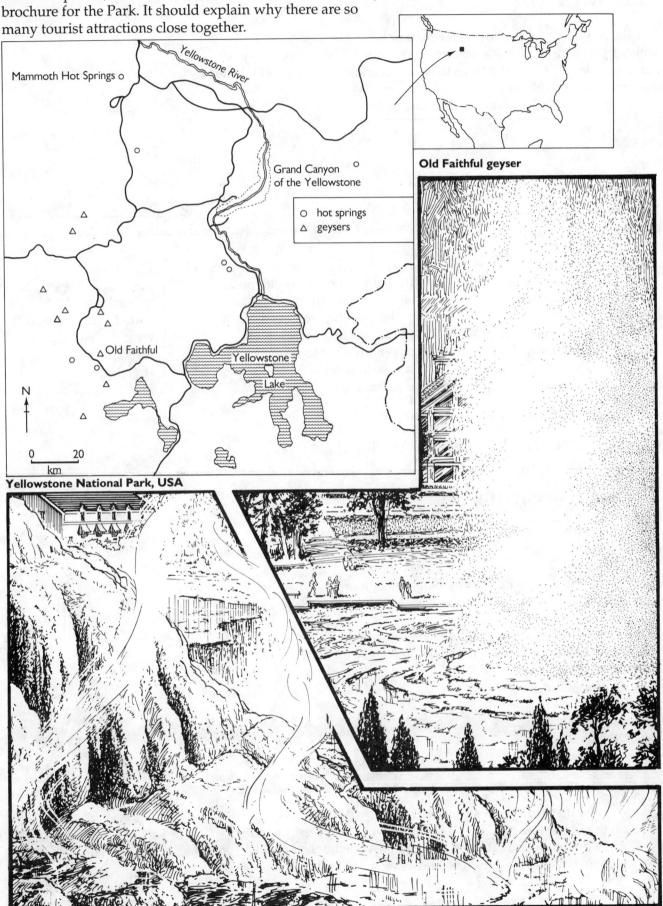

Old Faithful geyser

Yellowstone National Park, USA

hot springs ○
geysers △

Mammoth hot springs

30 Forces and strength

30.1 Stretching

Graphs A, B and C show how three materials stretch. Imagine that
you hang a piece of each material from a clamp. What happens if you
add equal weights, one at a time, to each material? Paragraphs D, E and F
describe what might happen.

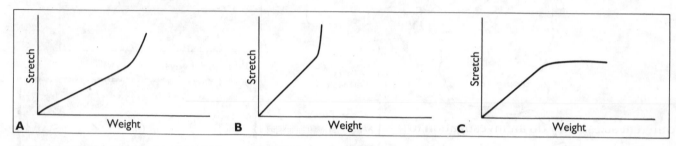

D At first, this material
stretches the same amount
when you add each weight.
This happens for several
weights. Then, extra weights
make it stretch more than
before.

E At first, this material stretches
the same amount when you add
each weight. After several
weights, extra weights make it
stretch more than before. It
never stretches as much as the
weakest material.

F At first, this
piece stretches evenly
for each weight
added. After several
weights, extra
weights hardly
stretch it at all.

a Which description goes with which graph?

b Which piece would make the best knicker elastic? Why?

30.2 Baby weighing

a Draw arrows to show the forces acting on the baby
while the nurse weighs it.

b Give two advantages of a spring balance compared
with kitchen scales.

c The nurse says the baby weighs 5560 grams. In fact,
this is the mass of the baby. What units do we use to
measure weight?

You need:
– pieces of elastic
– selection of weights
– ruler

Investigating

d The nurse's balance is a piece of elastic with hooks to clip
on to the baby's sheet. Will this elastic wear out? Design and
carry out an investigation to find out if over-stretched elastic
is more stretchy than fresh elastic. How would this affect
how it weighs the baby?

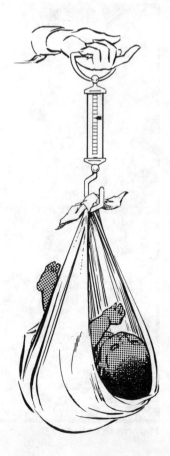

30.3 Cracking up

Many people like eating nuts. Anne wanted to know how much force she needs to crack different types of nuts. She fixed a forcemeter to the family's nutcrackers and did some tests.

Type of nut	Force (N)
walnut	20
Brazil nut	25
hazelnut	25
almond	50

a Draw a graph of Anne's results. Choose between a bar chart and a line graph. Explain your choice.

b What results do you think she would get with these larger nutcrackers? They are twice as long as her family's nutcrackers. Explain your answer carefully.

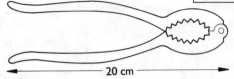

20 cm

30.4 Smashing

Jason and Kylie have five conkers of different sizes. They do an investigation to see whether big conkers are stronger than small ones.

They hold a brick 10 cm above the conker and drop it. They look to see if the conker is OK. If it is, they hold the brick at 20 cm and try again. They keep increasing the height of the brick until it smashes the conker.

They do this with each of their conkers. Here are their results.

Conker size (mm)	Height to smash (cm)
10	40
15	50
25	70
28	60
40	90

a Write a sentence explaining what their results show.

b One of their measurements looks a bit odd. Which one is it?

c Can you think of any ways of making this experiment more accurate?

Planning

d Kylie's neighbours said that they used to dry conkers in an oven to make them stronger. Plan an investigation to find the best temperature for drying the conkers.

30.5 Crushing

You need:
– card
– weights

a Design a box for carrying a cream cake. Use a piece of A4 card to make the box. Think about what a good box will do. Try a few designs and test each of them.

b Draw a diagram of your box to show the forces that act on it when it is crushed.

KS 3 Assessment Activities Pack A

31.1 Submarine and custard

'Let's see what you can do, then, Number 1,' said the captain of the submarine to his second-in-command. 'Bring her up to the surface.'

'Aye, aye, captain,' said Cool Joe, putting down his half-finished dish of custard, '**Blow bow tanks**.'

There was a hiss of compressed air as it forced the water out of the tanks at the front (the bow) of the submarine.

The submarine's bow angled sharply upwards, catching the captain by surprise. He tripped and fell face down on the deck.

Cool Joe was busy shouting orders. '**Blow stern tanks, flood bow**.'

This time the air rushed into the tanks at the back of the boat (the stern), while water sloshed into the front ones. The submarine shuddered and started to return to an even keel ... and then to slope the other way. The captain, still on the deck, holding his head and muttering to himself, saw the dish of cold custard slide off the table above him.

'Which idiot left this ... glug, glug, glug?' he gurgled.

Cool Joe was losing his cool. 'Flood stern tanks – no, blow them! Help, put the handbrake on!' he shouted, his voice rising as fast as the stern of the submarine.

Cool Joe hasn't quite got it right, has he?

a Use the idea of forces to explain why the boat behaved as it did after each instruction that is shown in dark print.

b Suppose you were the captain. What would you say to bring the boat to the surface?

31.2 Jane's snow shoes

Jane Beaver is tracking an escaped criminal, Mad Arnold. He broke out of jail and cycled to his hideout on White Ridge. Then the snow started to fall. Arnold thinks he is safe because the snow is now too deep to walk on. Anyone who tried would sink in and be trapped.

But Jane is wearing a pair of the new, top-secret snow shoes. These have a very large sole which spreads Jane's weight over a large area.

a Explain how Jane's shoes support her on the deep snow. Use the words *pressure*, *force* and *area* in your answer.

© Gott, Price, Thornley/Collins Educational 1992   *KS 3 Assessment Activities Pack A*

31.3 Falling

A good parachute falls as slowly as possible. Find out what makes a good parachute. You must not use a piece of material more than 30 cm × 30 cm.

Investigating

a Find out:

- Which is the best material?
- How many strings should the parachute have?

b How does the speed at which a parachute falls depend on the weight it is carrying? Use your best parachute to find out. Explain what your results mean.

Louise and Tom made parachutes from paper, cotton, plastic and silk. They dropped each one from a height of 3 metres. They timed how long the parachute took to reach the ground. Here are their results:

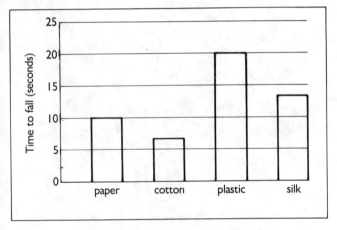

c How long did the paper parachute take to fall?

d How long did the silk parachute take to fall?

e Work out the speed at which each parachute fell to the ground.

f Draw a chart to show the speeds. Put the parachutes in order, with the slowest first.

g Draw a sketch of a falling parachute. Put arrows on your drawing to show the forces that affect the parachute as it falls. Each arrow should point in the direction that the force pulls. Label each arrow with the name of the force.

31.4 Fishing line

John wanted to find out how much two types of fishing line stretched with different weights on them. He had two spare lengths of line. Line A was 60 cm long, but the other, line B, was only 50 cm long. Here are his results.

Load (g)	Length of line A (cm)	Length of line B (cm)
0	50	60
100	55	64
200	60	68
300	65	72
400	70	76
500	75	80

a What is the length of line A with 400 g on it?

b How much longer is line B with 500 g on it than with no weight at all?

c Which fishing line was more stretchy? Explain how you worked out your answer.

d Hannah said, 'John should have measured the weight in newtons, not grams.' Is she right?

e Do a new table with the weight in newtons. Does it make any important differences to the results? The force on 100 g is 1 newton.

32.1 Stopping

The graph shows the total stopping distances for a car travelling at different speeds.

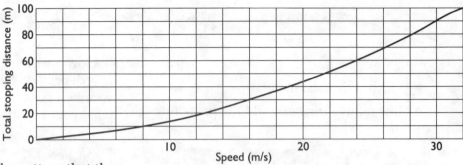

(graph: y-axis "Total stopping distance (m)" 0–100; x-axis "Speed (m/s)" 10, 20, 30)

a What is the total stopping distance when the car's speed is 20 metres per second?

b Write a sentence describing the pattern that the graph shows.

c What do you think the total stopping distance would be for a speed of 40 metres per second?

d Make a rough copy of the graph. On it, draw a line in a different colour to show the total stopping distance in wet or icy weather.

e Your mother is driving along the road when a cat runs out. The cat is 80 metres away. What is the fastest she could be driving if she can just stop in time?

f What forces make the car slow down to avoid hitting the cat?

g Draw a sketch of the car. Put arrows on your drawing to show the forces that affect the car when it is going at a steady speed. Each arrow should point in the direction that the force pulls or pushes. Label each arrow with the name of the force.

h Use ideas about forces to explain why it takes longer to stop if the road is icy.

32.2 How far?

Some toys have springs inside them that you can wind up with a key. As the spring unwinds, the toy moves. The spring is a store of energy. The more energy in the spring, the farther the car goes.

Planning

a Plan an investigation to find out:
- how the distance the toy moves depends on the number of turns of the key.
- if the number of turns of the key affects the speed of the car.

b What else might affect the way the car moves? Pick one of your ideas and test it.

KS 3 Assessment Activities Pack A

32.3 Which car?

The information below is about one range of Ford cars. The models offer a choice of features and engines. The table tells you about:
– whether the cars use petrol or diesel fuel,
– the cars' top speed,
– how quickly they can speed up,
– how much fuel they use,
– how much the cars weigh.

Look carefully at the table. Imagine that you have to advise drivers about buying the cars which suit their needs. Often they aren't sure whether to buy a diesel or a petrol car.

a Write a list of the good and bad things about petrol and diesel cars.

b A customer wants to buy a car to use as a taxi. What would you advise her to buy? Why?

c Which car has the greatest acceleration? Explain what acceleration means.

A joule of work is done when a force of 1 newton moves by 1 metre. The 1.3 petrol car needs a force of roughly 2500 newtons to accelerate from 0 to 60 m.p.h. in 13.5 seconds. The car covers roughly 180 metres in this time.

d How much work does the engine do in this time?

$$\text{The engine's power} = \frac{\text{work done}}{\text{time taken}}$$

e What is the power output of the engine?

Car type	Top speed (m.p.h.)	Acceleration 0–60 m.p.h. (s)	Fuel used at 56 m.p.h. (miles per gallon)	Mass (kg)
Three-door				
1.3 petrol	98	13.5	57.6	1275
1.6 diesel	91	16.6	70.6	1350
Five-door				
1.3 petrol	98	13.5	57.6	1300
1.6 diesel	91	16.6	70.6	1375
Three-door estates				
1.3 petrol	96	14.0	56.5	1350
1.6 diesel	89	17.1	68.9	1425
Five-door estates				
1.3 petrol	96	14.0	56.5	1350
1.6 diesel	89	17.1	68.9	1425

32.4 Hockey sticks

Gordon played hockey for the school team. He was good at dribbling, but he couldn't hit the ball very hard. A friend said that Gordon might be able to hit the ball harder with a heavier hockey stick. Gordon decided to try a heavier stick.

a Why might a heavy stick be better? Use ideas about forces in your answer.

Planning

b Write a plan for an investigation that Gordon could do to help him decide if a heavier stick is better. The plan should include a way to measure how much better a heavy stick is.

33 Electrical charge

33.1 Keep it clean!

Even a new LP soon gets dirty – the vinyl seems to attract fluff and dust, which spoils the sound.

Every time you pull a record out of its paper sleeve, it gives the record an electrostatic charge. This attracts dust. What can you do about it?

ELECTROCLOTH is the answer. Just one wipe over the record's surface and it destroys the charge.

Keep ELECTROCLOTH next to your record player and enjoy cleaner, clearer sounds!

Dustphree static spray coats your records with a thin layer of special chemicals. These stop static electricity from building up to give you a dust-free surface.

Dustphree – the solution to electrostatic dust!

a Record companies are going to print a warning on the sleeve of all vinyl records. This will explain why they are getting dusty. Use the information in the advertisements to help you. Design a series of simple diagrams (use as few words as possible) that they could use.

b Why do record companies use sleeves?

Lee tried to find out if the voltage on the record is affected by how wet the air is (the humidity). He also tried a few different materials for the record sleeve. His results are shown below.

Type of sleeve	Maximum voltage at 60% humidity (V)	Maximum voltage at 40% humidity (V)	Maximum voltage at 30% humidity (V)
acetate	500	700	1200
cellophane	400	600	1100
polythene	300	450	950
paper	80	300	500

c How does the humidity affect the voltage?

d Does it matter what material record companies use to make the sleeve? Explain your answer.

33.2 Shocking!

Cars build up static charge through friction with the road. These charges are usually too small to notice but sometimes they can give you a shock when you get out. Some cars have a strap that trails along the ground behind the car to discharge the static electricity.

a How does the strap work?

b What could the strap be made from? Suggest three different materials. List the advantages and disadvantages for each of them.

 KS 3 Assessment Activities Pack A

33.3 Hay fever

I hate summer! I get hay fever and, every June, my eyes feel dry and bloodshot, my nose runs and my throat itches. My body reacts badly to pollen from nettles and grasses. The plants release this pollen into the wind in the early summer. I try to stay indoors, but the pollen, which is just like fine dust, gets in anyway. There's no escape, and none of the medicines seem to work for me! It's like having a cold that lasts about six weeks! I hate summer!

Hay fever clears up very quickly when the pollen season is over. Even a few days away from the dust can help. Some people now buy electrostatic air filters. These have charged plates in them that attract the fine pollen grains and pull them out of the air. In this way, at least one room in the house can be kept fairly free of pollen.

Planning

a Plan an investigation to find out how the voltage on the plates affects how well the electrostatic filter clears the air.

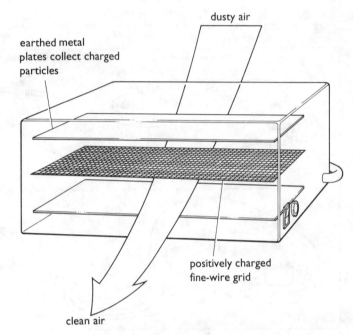

dusty air

earthed metal plates collect charged particles

positively charged fine-wire grid

clean air

33.4 Paper magic

Have you noticed that, if you rub a plastic comb, you can use it to pick up little bits of paper? It works because, when you rub the comb, it gets an electrostatic charge. The charge can be strong enough to attract paper.

You need:
– plastic comb or ruler
– duster or wool rag
– pieces of newspaper, 5 mm x 5 mm
– ruler to measure with

Investigating

a Find out:

● How many rubs do you need to make your comb pick up bits of paper?
● What is the greatest distance from which the comb will pick up bits of paper?
● Which other materials you can you use in the same way as the comb?
● Which other materials will the comb pick up?
● Can the comb pick up paper that is a little damp?

b Write up what you have found out.

c Use your ideas about electrostatic charges to explain your results.

KS 3 Assessment Activities Pack A

34.1 Circuits

a Copy out this table.

Circuit number	Series, parallel, or both?	What happens to bulb Y if you unscrew bulb X?
1		
2		
3		
4		
5		

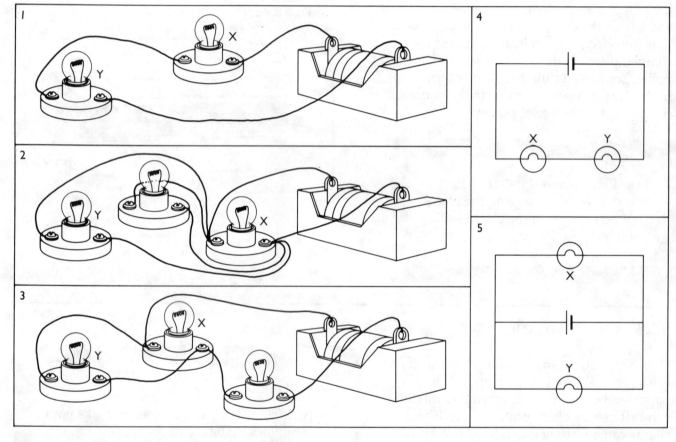

b Look at the five circuits. Decide if each one is a series circuit, a parallel circuit, or both. Fill in the second column of your table.

c Then decide what will happen to bulb Y if you unscrew bulb X in each circuit. Put the answer in your table.

d Draw a circuit symbol diagram for circuit 3.

e Make each of the circuits to check your answers.

34.2 Electricity memory test

a Explain what these words or phrases mean:
- electrical conductor,
- electrical insulator,
- electric current,
- potential difference (voltage),
- electrical resistance,
- parallel circuit,
- series circuit.

            KS 3 Assessment Activities Pack A

34.3 Let there be light ...

Here are advertisements for two electric light bulbs.

a You cannot check the advertisement for Brillo bulbs scientifically. Why not?

b You can check the claim for Everon scientifically. Write a plan to test the claim of the makers of the Everon bulbs.

34.4 Paying for it

Mr and Mrs Chauhan use electric storage radiators to keep their house warm. In October 1989, they had double glazing fitted to their house. They hoped this would save them money.

To see whether they have used less energy, because of the double glazing, they collected some of their past electricity bills. The readings are shown below.

Date of meter reading	Meter reading (units)	Number of units used in last 3 months
31 December 1988	08490	800
31 March 1989	09690	1200
30 June 1989	10490	800
30 September 1989	11090	600
Double glazing installed		
31 December 1989	11760	
31 March 1990	12810	
30 June 1990	13440	
30 September 1990	13920	

a Copy out and complete the table.

b Did the Chauhans use less energy after they had double glazing? How much less?

c Electricity cost about 6p per unit in 1990. How much money did the double glazing save them in 1990?

d Why does the amount of electricity they use vary through the year?

e Estimate the meter reading on 31 December 1990.

f The Chauhans tell their neighbour the double glazing is saving them money. Their neighbour is not so sure. What might the neighbour say to the Chauhans?

34.5 Let there be less light ...

You need:
- power pack
- torch bulb and holder
- connecting wire
- resistance wire
- electrical meter

a Design a dimmer switch for a torch.

b Build your dimmer switch and test it with a power pack and an ordinary torch bulb.

c Will the battery last longer if the bulb is dimmer? Plan and carry out an investigation to find out how the brightness of the bulb affects how long the battery lasts. (Hint: you do not have to wait for a battery to run down completely. Think about how else you could measure how much electrical energy the bulb uses.)

35.1 Electromagnets everywhere

a Work in a group. We use electromagnets in many situations.
Look at the diagrams. Discuss how each of the things works.

b Then, on your own, write an explanation of how each of the things
works. Your explanation must include what happens:
– when you close the switch,
– when you release the switch.

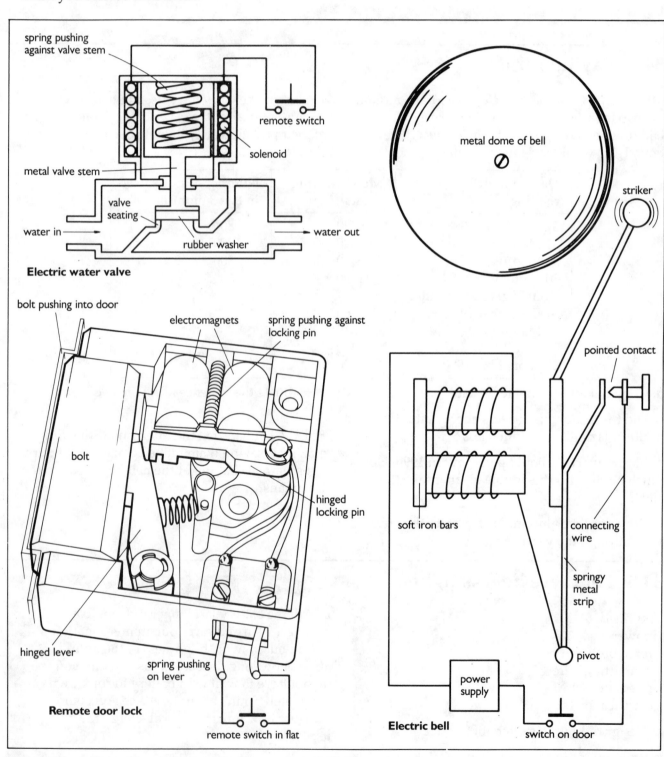

35.2 Powering the magnet

An electromagnet only works when electricity is flowing through it.

You need:
- power pack
- electromagnet
- connecting wire
- paper clips (steel)
- ammeter
- variable resistor

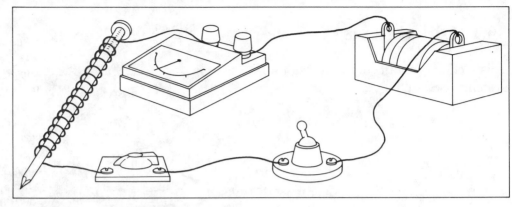

a Make a small electromagnet. Connect a variable resistor and an ammeter in the circuit with the electromagnet. Remember: only turn the circuit on when you need it.

b Find out the smallest current needed to hold five paper clips.

Investigating

c What affects how much weight your magnet will lift? In your group, make a list of things that would increase the weight that your magnet could lift. Pick your best idea and plan an investigation to test it.

When your teacher has checked your plan, carry it out.

35.3 Traffic lights

Cars contain so much metal that they act like magnets. Some traffic lights use loops of wire buried in the road to detect approaching cars.

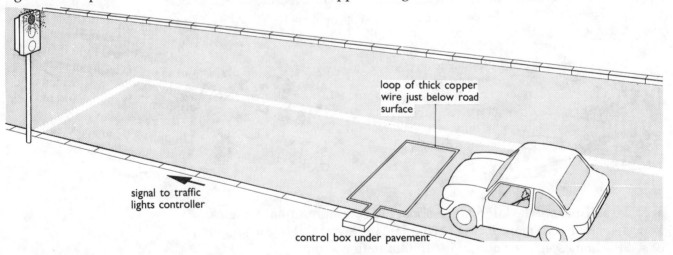

loop of thick copper wire just below road surface

signal to traffic lights controller

control box under pavement

a Explain fully what happens when the car drives over the wire loop.

Planning

b Can traffic lights detect motorcycles – or the smallest mopeds? Plan an investigation to find out how the size of the vehicle affects how easy it is for the sensor loop to detect it.

36.1 Old systems

This section is about communications systems used in the past.

Relays

Around 400 BC the Greeks used runners to carry written messages from one city to another. The runners ran a certain distance and then passed the  message to the next runner. In 1860, Buffalo Bill worked for the Pony Express in the USA. The route ran from St Jose in Missouri to Sacramento in California, a distance of about 4000 km. By using relays of ponies, a rider could cover 120 km in a day.

Light signals

In 490 BC the Persians attacked the Greek city of Athens. The Greeks were doing quite well until someone inside the city signalled coded messages to the Persians using a polished shield to reflect sunlight. Modern light signalling equipment uses large electric lamps with a range of 6 km in daylight and 18 km at night. Light travels at 300 000 km/s.

Talking drums

Many tribes in West Africa used drums to send messages from one village to another. Because  Africans passed their history on by word of mouth, rather than writing it down, we are not sure how old the method is. It could be one of the oldest ways of communicating over long distances. Sound travels at a speed of 330 m/s.

Coded flags

Around 500 BC the Phoenicians used to send messages by hanging their shields on the rigging of their boats.

 In 1805, Nelson used special flags at the battle of Trafalgar to send a message to all the sailors. He said, 'England expects every man to do his duty.' It took 15 minutes to hoist all the flags!

Beacons

In 1588, Spain threatened to invade England. As part of the defences, the English built a series of beacons. People kept a look-out for enemy ships. If they saw any,  they would light their beacon. The people at the next one would see it, and light theirs and so on. If the watchers had sighted the Spanish Armada off Cornwall, they could have sent a message to reach London, 400 km away, in 15 minutes.

a Make a display of the information about old communications systems. Your display should make it easy to compare the systems. For each method of sending a message, include (at least) information about:
– speed,
– distance,
– reliability.

You could also say something about:
– how easy it was to stop outsiders reading the message,
– how complicated the message can be.

b All the systems have three things in common. What are they?

36.2 Modern communication systems

Letter post

The letter post carries written documents (and colour pictures) very cheaply. Usually, the Post Office delivers a first class letter the day after you post it.

Telephone

The telephone can carry voice messages anywhere in the world. It can be expensive at peak times! Modern telephones can have answering machines to take messages while you are busy.

Fax

Fax machines can send still black and white pictures, as well as words. A fax machine uses a telephone line and takes about 15 seconds to send an A4 sized drawing.

Citizens-band radio

CB radio can carry messages up to 15 km away. A typical CB set costs less than £100 and there are no rental costs. The message travels at 300 000 km/s.

Radio pagers

Radio pagers cannot carry messages. They 'beep' to tell the person wearing them to phone their office immediately. They are much cheaper than mobile phones. The message travels at 300 000 km/s.

a Make a list of each of the methods of communicating. For each one, give an advantage and a disadvantage.

I don't see anyone all day when I'm out in the field ploughing. I get bored stiff! I'd like to be able to talk to other farmers in the area and don't suggest a mobile phone – I couldn't begin to afford the phone bills!

French is my favourite subject in school. I want to learn more about France through the eyes of an ordinary person, not from a book. I'd really like to have French friend of my own age.

I need to tell my customers when their cars are ready for them to collect. Sometimes I need to tell them they're not ready and save them a wasted journey! Most people want to know how much the work will cost before I start.

I am a heart specialist in a large hospital. I need to be everywhere at once! I do ward rounds like everyone else but, as soon as there's an emergency, I need to be in the intensive care unit. My colleagues must be able to get hold of me any time of the night or day – instantly.

I have to design parts for machines. Often, I end up trying to describe the components over the telephone. It doesn't really work! I need something that can send pictures and drawings quicker than the ordinary post.

b Suggest the best method of communicating for each person on this page. Give a reason for each choice.

c Design a database for a computer. It should contain all the relevant information about these modern communication systems and help people to find out which is the most suitable system for their needs.

37.1 Probes

A probe can be used to measure temperature. The table gives details of five types.

For each temperature measurement below, say which probe you would use and why.

a A human body.

b A freezer in a shop.

c A pottery kiln.

d A greenhouse.

e The soil, 30 cm below the surface.

Probe	Temperature range (°C)		Sensitivity * least sensitive **** most sensitive
	minimum	maximum	
A	–10	115	**
B	25	45	****
C	–10	45	***
D	0	1000	*
E	–40	10	***

37.2 Analogue and digital

Read the article and answer the questions.

a What did CD players cost when manufacturers first introduced them?

b How much more expensive was a CD than an LP five years ago?

c How many times more expensive are CDs than LPs now?

d What is the main disadvantage of CD players?

e Why have the costs of CD players and discs fallen in the last five years?

f Give one difference between the digital and analogue signals shown in the article.

g Suggest a fair way of deciding if a CD or a DAT produces the better sound quality.

37.3 Home electronics

a Make a list of all the things in your house that use microelectronics.

b Ask your parents what electrical things they had in their homes when they were your age. Make a list.

c What sort of things do you think your children might have in their homes when they reach your age?

DAT – the most important advance since CD?

digital signal

analogue signal

When the recording industry released compact discs barely five years ago, a CD player cost anything between £400 and £500. The few discs that were available cost about £15. A good quality record deck would have been £85 at the time and vinyl LPs £6. Despite this, CDs were a massive success. Over half of the recorded music material purchased by the public now is on CD and players now cost between £100 and £200. But CD has its problems. The main one must be that you cannot record on CD in the home. Digital audio tape (DAT) may be about to change that. DAT uses a digital signal but can record on ordinary tape. This means the sound quality is as good as CD and you can now make digital recordings at home. DAT players are expensive at the moment, perhaps £350 for a middle-of-the-range machine, but they will get cheaper over the next few years.

Does this mean that CD will soon go the way of vinyl records? In five years' time, will people be taking home DAT copies of Cliff Richard for Christmas?

© Gott, Price, Thornley/Collins Educational 1992   *KS 3 Assessment Activities Pack A*

37.4 Logic gates

Look at the logic circuits on page 87 of *Active Science Book 3*.

Draw a logic system for each of the following problems. The first one is drawn for you as an example.

a I work in a factory with a powerful lathe. It must have a safety system so that I have to press both the button and the foot switch before the lathe starts to turn.

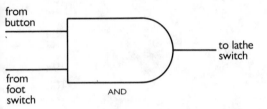

from button

to lathe switch

from foot switch

AND

b It is always dark when I get home, and I've reversed into the stuff in my garage once already! I need a parking light which will come on when it's dark and when I have opened the garage door.

c I am a security guard at a large office building. There are two main entrances. I want a light to go on when someone opens either door.

d I work for British Telecom. I need a circuit that will turn on a light in a telephone box. The light must only come on at night when someone is in the box.

e I have to keep my eye on separate displays of personal stereos and calculators. I want a light to go on to warn me if someone is fiddling with the stereos or the calculators.

37.5 Instruments

Watches with hands, and mercury thermometers, have been fine for many years. We call them analogue instruments. Some modern watches and thermometers give numbers in their display. We call these digital instruments.

Here is a list of some analogue and digital devices:

What it measures	Analogue	Digital
Temperature	mercury thermometer	electronic thermometer
Electric current	meter with moving needle scale	meter with digital display
Speed	speedometer with moving pointer	speedometer with digital display

a Add three more pairs to the list.

b For each pair in the list, write down the advantages of the analogue instrument and the advantages of the digital instrument.

Analogue watch

Digital watch

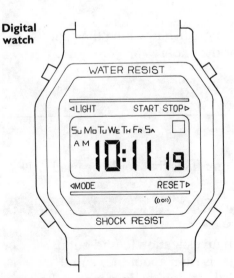

38 Fuels

38.1 Washing clothes

Jim and Anne bought an electric boiler to heat water for washing clothes in their caravan. They wanted to know how long it would take to get the water hot. They filled it with cold water and borrowed a thermometer to check its temperature. This is what they found:

(They forgot to take the temperature at 5 minutes!)

a Make a display of their results. Use a pie chart, a bar chart or a line graph – whichever you think is best.

b Use your display to work out the temperature after 5 minutes.

c These labels are from their washing. How long should they heat the water for the clothes and for the underwear?

Time from switching on (min)(°C)	Temperature (°C)
0	10
1	14
2	30
3	45
4	59
5	-
6	84
7	93
8	98
9	100
10	100

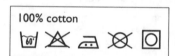

Washing labels from clothes

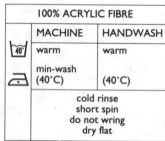

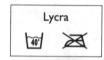

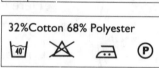

Underwear washing labels

The next batch was mainly underwear. They needed only half as much water this time.

Investigating

d Plan and carry out an investigation to find out how the amount of water affects the time it takes to warm up.

e Use your results to predict how long the boiler should be left on for the underwear.

38.2 Some like it hot

'My father is a plumber. He says that it is better to leave our gas central-heating boiler turned on all day and all night. This will keep the house warm all the time. The boiler will not have to work so hard heating up the house from cold. Leaving it on all the time saves energy.

My mother is a heating engineer. She says that my dad is wrong. We should just run the boiler when we need heat in the mornings and evenings. I do not know who is right. What do you think?'

a List the different fuels that could be used to heat a home.

Planning

b Plan an investigation to find out if my mother is right about the central heating. What might make your results inaccurate?

 KS 3 Assessment Activities Pack A

38.3 A burning question ... AS 2

Look at the information about camping stoves on page 46 of *Active Science 2*.
A group of students going on an expedition decided to test the stoves. They
boiled 200 cm³ of water on
each one. They measured
how long it took and how
much fuel they used.

Stove	Time taken	Fuel used (g)	Cost of 100 g of fuel (p)
Trangia	4 min	10	15
Solid fuel	12 min	20	30
Primus	3 min (once lit)	10	5
Camping gas	5 min	20	50

a Work out what it cost to
boil the water with each fuel.
b The students used 200 cm³
of water with each fuel. What other things should they have done to make
sure that it was a fair test?
c What safety precautions should they have taken?
d Look at the information about each fuel at the top of page 47 of *Active
Science 2*. Which of the stoves would you take on a walking and camping
expedition? Explain your choice.

38.4 How much do we have left?

Study the tables of energy use and energy production.

Estimated energy use for 1990 in millions of tonnes of oil equivalent

	Solid fuel	Oil	Natural gas	Other	Total
European Community	242	441	190	161	1034
USA	633	753	484	179	2049
Japan	71	219	49	66	405
Other industrial countries	236	295	109	129	769
Arab oil producers	2	85	65	6	158
Other countries	165	633	160	573	1531
USSR	375	510	535	70	1490
China	560	90	15	78	743
Eastern Europe	408	117	116	39	680
World total	2692	3143	1723	1301	8859

Estimated energy production for 1990 in millions of tonnes of oil equivalent

	Solid fuel	Oil	Natural gas	Other	Total
European Community	175	111	115	162	563
USA	718	454	432	179	1783
Japan	10	2	0	66	78
Other industrial countries	321	153	154	128	756
Arab oil producers	0	878	88	6	967
Other countries	119	843	200	573	1735
USSR	375	625	625	70	1695
China	560	100	15	78	753
Eastern Europe	415	18	55	39	527
World total	2693	3179	1684	1301	8857

a Which region produces the most energy?
b Which region uses the most gas?
c Which region produces no coal?
d Worldwide oil reserves are 85 000 million tonnes.
How long will they last, if we use them at the
present rate?
e Many things could alter our present rate of
using oil. What things would make the oil run out:
– sooner than you expect?
– later than you expect?

f Oil, coal and natural gas are the decayed
remains of living things. My teacher says that this
means they all came from solar energy in the first
place. Explain what he means.
g Solid fuel, oil and natural gas are
non-renewable energy sources. What does
non-renewable mean?

39 Energy transfers

39.1 What's the source?

a What provides the energy to run each of these objects?

Here are some ways of telling that something is using energy·
– it moves,
– it gets hot,
– it makes a noise,
– it lights up.

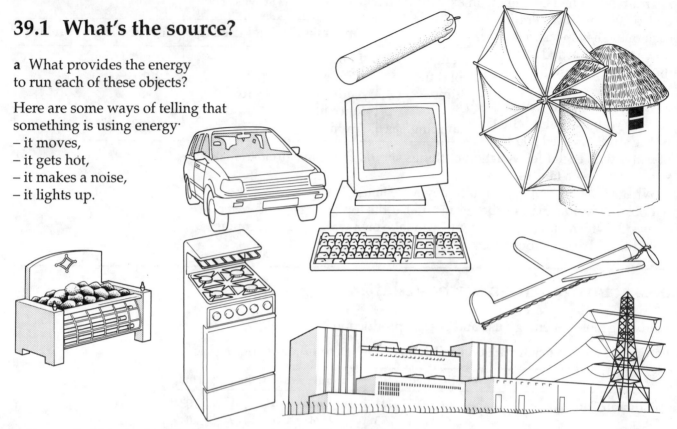

b For each object in the diagram, how can you tell that it is using energy when it is working?

c Each object shown changes energy from one form to another. Draw a flow chart for three of the

objects to show the energy changes. Always start with the source energy.

d 'Energy is not destroyed or created.' Use one of your flow charts to explain what this means.

39.2 Vroooooooommm!

This toy car uses a flywheel to make it go. You push it along the ground a few times to get the flywheel turning fast. Then you put it down, and you let it go. Vroooooooommm!

a What is the energy source that makes the car move?

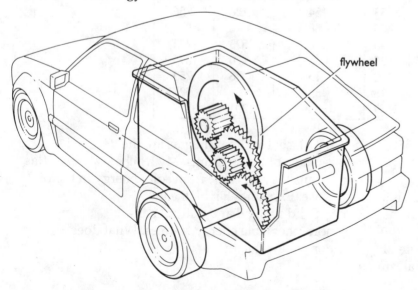

flywheel

Planning

b A flywheel is a heavy wheel inside the car. Once it starts turning, it takes a long time to stop. Plan an investigation to find out how the speed of the flywheel affects the distance the car can travel.

c A rival toy firm makes a car with a flywheel that is twice as wide and so is twice as heavy. How would this car behave differently from the first one?

© Gott, Price, Thornley/Collins Educational 1992   KS 3 Assessment Activities Pack A

39.3 Energy efficiency of washing machines

Washing machine data

Model	Price (£)	Maximum load (kg)	Maximum spin (rpm)	Energy used cotton wash (MJ)	Energy used synthetics (MJ)	Water used cotton wash (litres)
A	365	5.0	850	5.4	2.2	103
B	335	4.0	500	9.4	2.9	84
C	380	4.0	800	10.1	1.8	113
D	295	4.0	800	5.8	0.7	90
E	355	4.0	550	5.4	1.8	64
F	283	5.0	800	4.7	2.9	105
G	365	5.0	1200	5.0	1.8	100
H	384	5.0	1300	4.7	1.4	110
I	295	5.0	800	6.1	3.2	93
J	315	5.0	1100	6.5	4.0	95
K	375	4.0	1000	6.5	2.2	100
L	795	5.0	1100	9.0	3.6	100

Look at the information about washing machines. Now try these questions:

a When it is working, a washing machine turns electrical energy into other forms of energy. What are these other forms of energy?

b Explain what an advertisement means when it says 'This washing machine is energy efficient.'

c A class of 14-year-olds made these comments about washing machines. For each one, say if you think it is true. Write down evidence from the table to support your answer.
- Washing machines that take larger loads always need more electricity.
- More expensive machines are more efficient.

39.4 Energy memory test

a Explain what these words mean:
– conduction,
– convection,
– radiation.

b Use the idea of moving particles to explain how heat is transferred along an iron bar.

c Think of two materials which are used because they conduct heat:
– very well,
– very badly.

39.5 Energy transfers

Here is a list of heat transfers for a house:

a Sort the heat transfers into three lists due to: conduction, convection and radiation.

b Underline those where heat is *lost* by the house.

c Pick three of the energy losses and explain how each loss could be cut down.

d A double glazing company says that installing double glazing will save you money. What information do you need to decide if this is true?

> sunlight through windows
> energy passing through walls
> energy passing through the roof
> energy passing through the floor
> wasteheat from electrical appliances
> energy from an electric bar fire
> draughts under the front door
> draughts around badly-fitting windows

40.1 Does everything melt when it gets hot?

You need:
– selection of substances from your teacher

Observing

Find out how things behave when they get hot. You will need to observe closely what happens to each substance:
– before you heat it,
– as it gets hot,
– as it cools down,
– when it is cold.

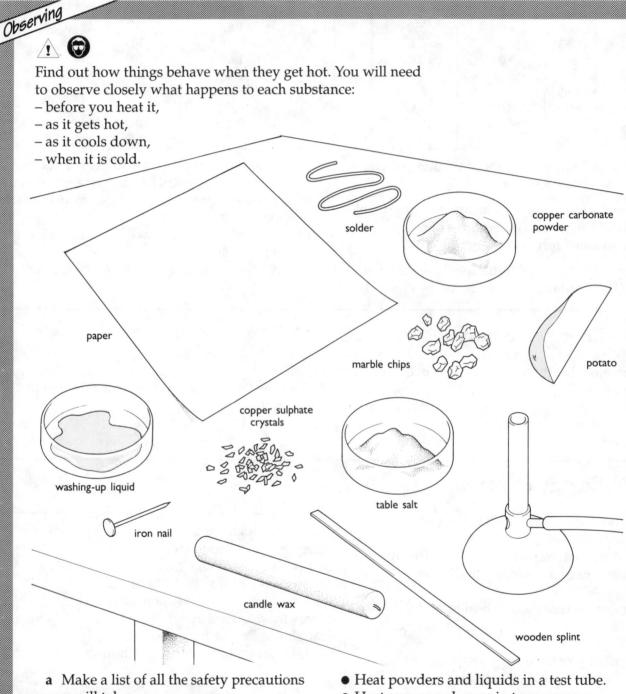

solder

copper carbonate powder

paper

marble chips

potato

copper sulphate crystals

washing-up liquid

table salt

iron nail

candle wax

wooden splint

a Make a list of all the safety precautions you will take.

b Organise a way of recording your results.

c Heat a small amount of each substance in turn.

● Heat powders and liquids in a test tube.
● Heat papers or lumps in tongs or on a tin lid.

d Sort the substances into groups (no more than five), based on what happened to them. Explain how you decided what should go into each group.

40.2 Estimating temperature

Sketch the thermometer in your book.

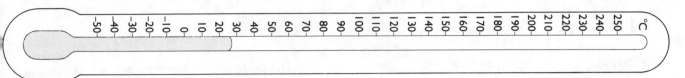

For each of the temperatures below, mark a letter on your sketch in the right place.
(Careful: there are one or two trick questions!)

a Room temperature.
b A freezer.
c Your body temperature.
d The middle of a fridge.
e A hot oven.

f A hot bath.
g Boiling water.
h A hot day.
i Iced water.

40.3 Toffee apples

a Heat some sugar on a tin lid. Describe very carefully everything that happens. How many changes does the sugar go through?

Making toffee is quite easy, but making toffee apples is not! The toffee must be hot enough to flow round the apple, but not drip off before it has hardened. If the toffee gets too hot, it will burn.

Planning

b Plan an investigation to find out the best temperature for toffee for toffee apples.

c Look at the recipe for toffee apples. What does it tell you about checking when the toffee is ready?

Making toffee

1. Put 750 g of demerara sugar, 75 g of margarine, 175 ml of water, 2 teaspoons of vinegar and 2 tablespoons of golden syrup in a clean saucepan.

2. Heat the mixture, stirring gently until it boils. Boil for 5 minutes without stirring. Be careful: it burns very easily!

3. When the toffee seems right, take it off the heat and test it.

4. To test the toffee, drop a teaspoonful of the mixture into a mug of cold water. If it feels firm, but not too hard when you take it out of the water, it is probably right.

5. Dip the apples into the toffee and then put them on a greased baking tray to cool.

41.1 Gears

The diagram shows the gears on a racing bicycle.

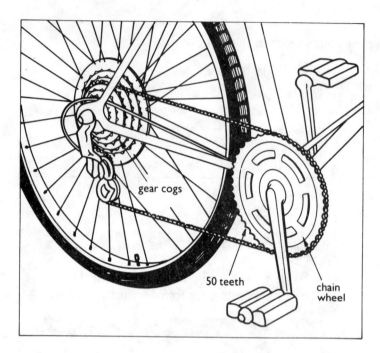

The table shows the number of teeth on each of the cog wheels.

Gear cogs	Number of teeth
chain wheel	50
first gear	25
second gear	20
third gear	16
fourth gear	13
fifth gear	10

a When the bicycle is in first gear, the chain is on the chain wheel and the first-gear cog. How many times will the back wheel turn for each turn of the pedals?

b What difference will changing from first to second gear make? Explain why it makes this difference.

c If you turn the pedals at the same rate, how much faster will you go in fifth gear than you will in first gear?

41.2 Upwardly mobile

You will need:
- source of energy (a battery and motor)
- wheels
- construction materials

a Make a machine to transport a golf ball up a slope 1 metre long rising by 30 cm.

b Explain how your machine needs to change if the slope is replaced by two steps 1 metre long with a rise of 30 cm.

c Whose machine is most efficient?

© Gott, Price, Thornley/Collins Educational 1992   *KS 3 Assessment Activities Pack A*

41.3 Gas taps

I have had arthritis for years. Most of the time I don't notice it, but sometimes I get very bad pain in my joints. My hands and ankles are the worst. Sometimes I feel as if I can't even get out of bed, let alone come to school! In science lessons I can manage all the equipment except the gas tap. It's having to press the little button at the side and turn the tap at the same time that's difficult.

Design and build an aid for Mary. It should help her to turn on the gas tap by herself. You could test it by trying to turn on the gas tap while you are wearing boxing gloves!

41.4 Groovy gears

Look carefully at the drawings of model gears and try to work out what they do.

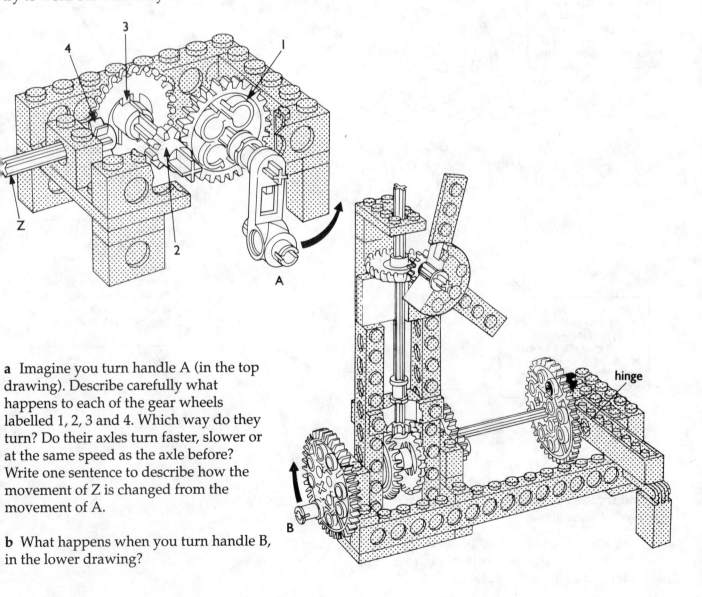

a Imagine you turn handle A (in the top drawing). Describe carefully what happens to each of the gear wheels labelled 1, 2, 3 and 4. Which way do they turn? Do their axles turn faster, slower or at the same speed as the axle before? Write one sentence to describe how the movement of Z is changed from the movement of A.

b What happens when you turn handle B, in the lower drawing?

42.1 Thunder and lightning AS1

During a thunderstorm over Leicester, there was one very large bolt of lightning. It may have badly damaged a building. On this street map of Leicester, the taller buildings are black.

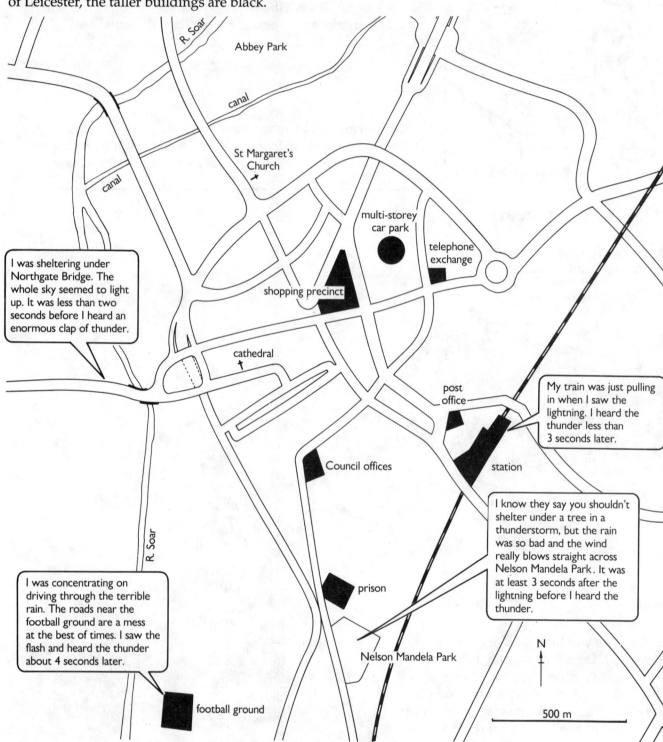

a Study the map and the comments. Work out where the lightning struck. Sound travels at 330 m/s. Light travels at 300 000 000 m/s. Explain how you arrived at your answer.

b Read about the causes of thunder on page 125 of *Active Science 1*. Use three or four sketches, with labels, to explain to a friend why thunder and lightning happen.

42.2 Musical instruments

a Look at the photograph of the street musician on page 66 in *Active Science 2*. For each instrument he is playing, write down:

- how it makes sounds
- how you could make the sound louder
- how you could make a higher-pitched sound

b Read page 64 of *Active Science 2* about how sound travels. Write a few lines to explain how you can hear what the street musician plays.

c When the street musician hits the drum, energy is transferred from the drum to the air. How do we detect this energy?

42.3 Three blind mice?

We interviewed The Great Silico just before his nightclub turn in Gateshead. He told us that he started playing tunes on wine glasses when he was five ...

'At first, I just rubbed my Dad's wine glass rim with a wet finger. I found that a full glass gave a much higher note than an empty one. I got a few thick ears when I spilt my Dad's best claret. I even broke a glass once with a top G. I soon had a set of glasses, tuned to play all sorts of popular music. Money, fame, stardom and my own Christmas TV special were just round the corner.'

a The TV company will record Silico's Christmas special in November for transmission over Christmas. Make a flow chart showing what happens to the sounds before they reach the viewers. We have started the chart for you:

The Great Silico rubs the top of the wine glass with a wet finger ⇒ Wine glass vibrates ⇒ Vibrating glass makes air vibrate → Microphone picks up vibrations in air and converts then to electrical signals

b Use different colours, on your chart, to show where:
– the signal is a sound,
– the signal is electrical,
– the signal is a radio wave.

c How does the loudspeaker in your TV set work? Look at *Active Science 3*, page 79. Now explain it all to the person next to you.

42.4 Sounds familiar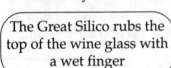

Look at page 67 in *Active Science 2*. It tells you about oscilloscopes. They can display a sound as a signal on a screen.

Match the sounds below to the displays on the oscilloscope. Give reasons for your choices.

a James playing a single, clear note on a flute.
b 'Whistling' Molly Segwave doing her version of 'The 1812 Overture'.
c Sheila playing her electric bass guitar.
d Errol blowing his dog whistle.
e Ian dropping a tin tray on a stone floor.
f Jasmine using her fire engine's siren.

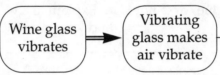

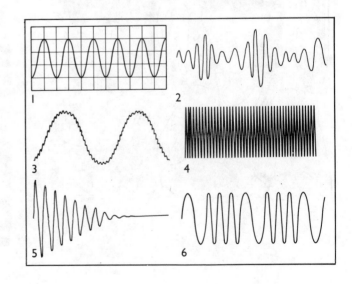

KS 3 Assessment Activities Pack A

43.1 All bunged up

a Make a list of the problems that a cold can cause.

b Does a child with a cold find it easier to hear high-pitched sounds or low-pitched sounds?

c Why might a doctor give nose drops for ear ache?

Glue ear is common in small children. Glue ear is like having a constant head cold. The sticky fluid does not clear from the ear. Decongestants can help. In the worst cases, the doctor will push little tubes, called grommets, into the ear drum to drain the liquid away. The hearing loss, caused by untreated glue ear, makes a child take longer to learn to talk. So, although glue ear is not serious, doctors must detect it early.

Nurse Doris' helpline

Ms N from Macclesfield writes:
'When one of my children gets a cold, the others always catch it. To make matters worse, it seems they all go deaf together! It's a pain but my neighbour says the children can't come to any real harm. Is she right?'

I am afraid not, Ms N. Our own doctor explains:

'Mucus collects in the tubes in the head to give a bunged up feeling. It's probably the worst part of any bad cold. Thick, sticky liquid fills the tubes behind the throat leading to the ear. Sometimes it even fills the delicate middle ear cavity. This can stop the ear drum and ear bones from doing their job properly. Sounds don't get through to the inner ear - we can even feel slightly deaf for a while. The condition affects high-pitched sounds worse than low sounds. In the worst cases bacteria grow in this liquid. These bacteria can cause a lot of pain and damage the inner ear.'

This sounds a bit worrying but there's no need to panic. You can help yourself **and** your children by giving them a gentle decongestant. It helps to clear the tubes and so reduce the dangers of infection. Your children will get over their colds that bit more quickly.

But do remember: you are not curing earache. **Always** consult your doctor if earache lasts more than 8 hours. ∎

d Describe any problems you can imagine when using a hearing test with a 3-year-old.

e Explain to a worried parent how the ear works and why grommets may be needed for his child.

43.2 Personal stereos

Have you ever tried to sleep on a train journey? Sounds OK, but have you tried to sleep near passengers using personal stereos? Everyone else can hear them as well.

Investigating

You need:
– personal stereo
– materials to test

a Find out which materials stop the noise leaking out. You will need to do some tests – but do not stick anything in your ear. Write up the tests you do and give your results.

b Design a personal-stereo headphone, showing how you could cut down the amount of noise leaking out. Suggest materials for the different parts.

43.3 Health and safety at work

Ted worked in a steel mill from the age of 16. His job was to look after a giant rolling mill as it turned steel ingots into sheet steel. He retired in 1975 at the age of 49 because of ill health. His hearing is now so poor he cannot hear normal conversation. His doctor thinks the noise of heavy machinery at work damaged his hearing. Ted is wondering whether to try to get compensation from his employer.

Wave forms

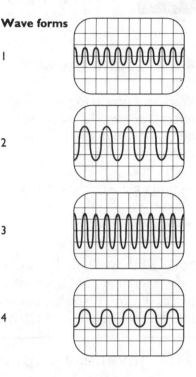

a What other things might have caused Ted's hearing loss?

Planning

b Plan an investigation to find out if there is a connection between loud noises and deafness. You cannot try to make people deaf. Think about:
– what sort of information you would need to collect,
– where you could find this information,
– how you could interpret this information.

c Modern factories provide ear protectors for workers in noisy areas. If a worker does not use these protectors, and is deafened, should the firm pay compensation? Work in a group to list the arguments on both sides.

d On your own, imagine you are the judge who has to decide the case. Write your summing-up of the arguments and give your judgement, with reasons.

e The damage done by a sound depends on its loudness and pitch. Loud, high-pitched sounds are most annoying and dangerous. The wave forms shown here are samples of sounds from different parts of a steel foundry. Make a list, putting the most dangerous areas at the top.

44 Using light

44.1 Light show

Work in a group to prepare some lighting effects for a model stage. You can use any old bits and pieces, but you will probably find these useful:
– a mirror,
– empty glass or clear plastic containers,
– some water,
– any glass object,
– any clear plastic object.

Make a beam of light by blocking off the light from a torch or light bulb with two books or pieces of card. If you are using a mains bulb, do not put the book or card too near it. Why not?

a Now find ways with your bits and pieces to:
– turn the beam round a corner,
– make a rainbow,
– make the beam narrower (focus it),
– make the beam spread out.

b Draw a sketch, with a brief description, for each effect.

c What changes would you have to make to put the light show on in a large theatre?

d Use the idea that light travels as waves to explain why a beam of light bends as it passes into a glass of water.

44.2 Javanese puppets

The Mahabharata is a famous story told in many countries. In Java, they tell it using puppets which are flat. The puppeteers sometimes cut them from leather, but they make the best ones of silver. A lamp casts shadows of the puppets on a screen. The audience sits in front of the screen and the puppeteers are behind the screen. The beautiful puppets are only seen by very important guests. Most of the audience only see the shadows.

You need:
– card (to make puppets)
– craft knife or scissors (to cut out puppets) ⚠
– projector (or other light source)
– screen (not opaque)
– metre rule

Investigating

a Plan and carry out an investigation to find out the best position for the puppet, lamp and screen below.

b Suggest a reason for your findings.

   KS 3 Assessment Activities Pack A

44.3 Cameras

The diagram shows a section through a camera.

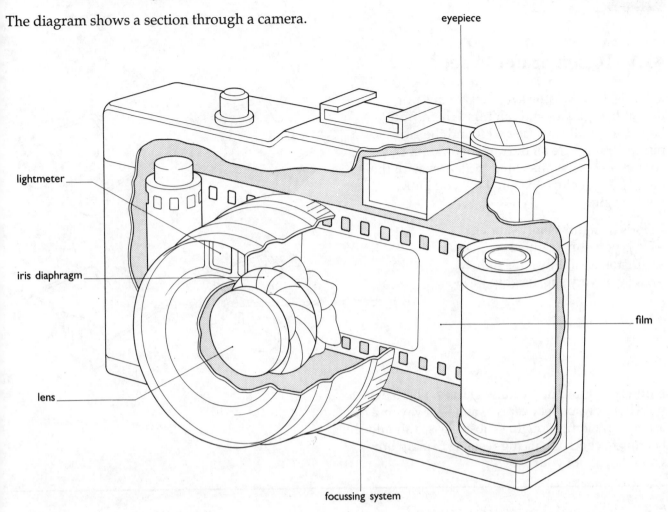

eyepiece

lightmeter

iris diaphragm

lens

film

focussing system

a Make a list of the labelled parts and write down what each one does.

b Complete the table. It matches the parts of your eye and a camera that do the same job. The picture on page 62 of *Active Science* 2 may help you.

Eye	Camera
the retina	the film
	iris diaphragm
	lens
	lens cap

44.4 Spotlights

Modern rooms often have spotlights in the ceiling, pointing to different parts of the room. A simple spotlight is just an ordinary light bulb in a tube, like those in the diagrams.

a Copy the diagrams. On each one, draw where the light will shine. The first one is done for you.

b Should inside the tube be shiny or black? Explain your answer.

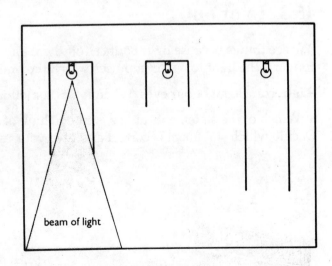

beam of light

45.1 To see or not to see?

a Doris, Flo, Winston and Sanjay have put down their glasses and can't find them. You have come to the rescue and found the glasses, but the frames are all the same. Work out the correct owners by matching the lenses with the descriptions below. Explain how you know you're right.

– Doris is slightly short-sighted.
– Flo is very long-sighted.
– Winston is slightly long-sighted.
– Sanjay is very short-sighted.

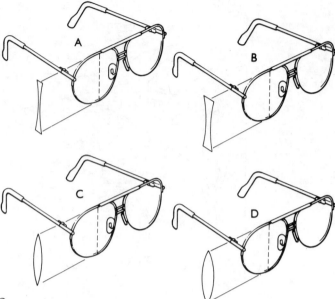

b Ethel can't find her reading glasses. She'd have to hold her newspaper over two metres away, but her arms aren't long enough! Whose glasses should she borrow to check the racing results? Explain how you worked out your answer.

45.2 School-industry links?

Quicksight are a company that sell lenses for spectacles. They are preparing a publicity leaflet to be given away in the local shopping centre. It will advertise their services.

The Marketing Director for Quicksight also wants to give these leaflets to libraries, schools, hospitals and opticians. He has promised to use one side of the leaflet to explain how the human eye works.

Design the 'explanation side'. The leaflet will be A4 size and it will be printed in full colour.

45.3 In or out?

'We see things because light bounces off them and into our eyes. The eye converts the light to nerve impulses which the brain can understand.'

'Light comes out of our eyes. When it hits something, we can see it.'

a Which of the statements above is true? Think of a way to find out. Decide which statement is correct and give your reasons.

© Gott, Price, Thornley/Collins Educational 1992   *KS 3 Assessment Activities Pack A*

46.1 The complete spectrum

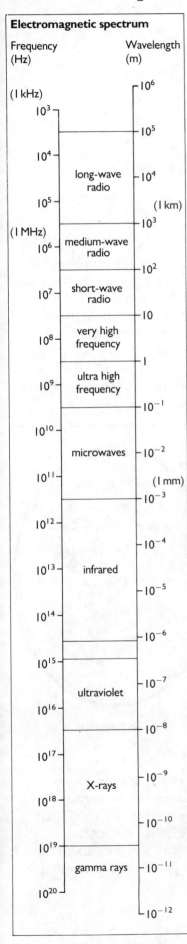

Electromagnetic spectrum

Here is a complete electromagnetic spectrum. It shows the frequency and wavelength of all electromagnetic waves.

a Sketch the electromagnetic spectrum in your book. All these objects produce electromagnetic waves:

A The Sun.
B Hot fire.
C Street lamp.
D Hospital X-ray machine.
E Microwave oven.

F Nuclear reactor.
G TV transmitter.
H Shortwave radio.
I Police speed trap.

Put the letter of each object in the right place on your electromagnetic spectrum.

b Choose one machine from the list above and explain how it uses radiation.

46.2 Microwave ovens

Cold spots and food poisoning

Check your microwave. Some ovens heat the food in parts but can leave cold spots where the microwave radiation does not reach. These cold spots could offer bacteria the chance to grow. Experts say there is little risk but suggest the following ways to reduce the risk even further:

- Have your microwave serviced regularly by qualified engineers.
- Do not overload the turntable so that it cannot move properly.
- Never let food hang over the edge of the turntable.
- Do not be tempted to cut down the cooking times.

Leaking microwaves

Microcooker today recalled large numbers of the microwave ovens it sold between January 1989 and March 1990. A company spokesperson explained that the danger of microwave radiation leaking from the oven was very small but, in the interests of public safety, they were taking no chances. Customers will have their ovens checked and returned to them (or replaced) within a three-week period.

Microwave cooking

Microwave ovens work by passing microwave radiation through food. This radiation contains energy which can be absorbed by water molecules in the food. These molecules start to move more quickly and so the food heats up. Since microwaves deliver the heat into the centre of the food, the item cooks much more quickly than when the heat is from the outside. Microwave ovens also use a lot less energy than conventional electric cookers.

a Work in a group to list the advantages and disadvantages of microwave cooking.

b Explain how each of the suggestions in the article, 'Cold spots and food poisoning', will help to reduce the risk of food poisoning.

c How does a microwave oven cook food? Prepare a simple explanation for the manufacturer to put in their instructions booklets. Use diagrams and up to 100 words.

d Many microwave ovens have an electric heating element. This browns the food. Why don't the microwaves do this?

e How could you test (safely) if a microwave oven 'leaks'? Do a plan.

47.1 Sunspots [AS 3]

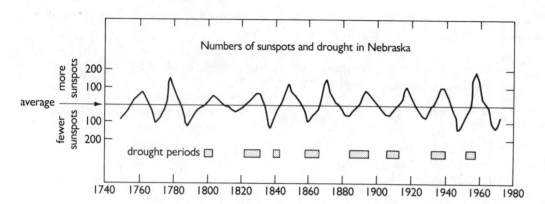

Numbers of sunspots and drought in Nebraska

Page 136 in *Active Science 3* will help you with these questions.

a You should never look directly at the sun. Why?

b What are sunspots?

c Why did European scientists refuse to believe sunspots existed even though they could clearly see them through telescopes?

Many people have tried to link the number of sunspots to changes in the weather on Earth. Look at the information given in the graph.

d Quote some evidence from the graph that suggests sunspots do affect the weather.

e Quote some evidence that suggests sunspots do not affect the weather.

f Do you think sunspots affect the weather? Give reasons for your answer.

47.2 Changing views

Nicolaus Koppernigk (1473-1543)

Copernicus (the Latin form of Koppernigk) was the first European to suggest that the Earth was not the centre of the universe. He wrote a book called *Concerning the revolutions of the celestial spheres* but was afraid people would laugh at his ideas. He finished the book in 1533, but did not publish it until 1543 when he was dying. A Lutheran minister wrote a foreword which explained that the ideas in the book were a 'mathematical game' which was useful for working out the positions of the planets; they did not mean the Earth really moved round the Sun. In fact, Copernicus did believe that the planets revolved round the Sun. He thought they must move in circular orbits because circles were perfect shapes. He believed that heavenly bodies could only move in paths that were perfect shapes.

Copernicus

Tycho Brahe

Tycho Brahe (1546-1601)

Tycho Brahe was a Danish astronomer and astrologer who thought Copernicus' theories were wrong. He put forward his own theory that the planets revolved round the Sun, and that the Sun and Moon revolved round the Earth. His most important work was to collect vast amounts of data about the positions of stars and planets. He was particularly interested in the movements of the planet Mars.

© Gott, Price, Thornley/Collins Educational 1992   *KS 3 Assessment Activities Pack A*

Johannes Kepler (1571-1630)

Kepler was a student of Tycho Brahe's. When Brahe died, all the information he had collected passed to Kepler. Kepler tried to explain all these observations, using Brahe's complicated model. It did not work. When he looked at Copernicus' ideas they seemed only slightly better. Eventually, in 1609, he published a book that brought together all the relevant observations in one model. Kepler wrote that the planets go round the Sun but their orbits are ellipses not circles.

Kepler

Galileo Galilei (1564-1642)

Galileo was the first European to study the skies with a telescope. He collected evidence for ten years, between 1609 and 1619. His first major discovery was that the planet Jupiter had moons – he counted four of them through his telescope. He imagined this as a small model of the complete solar system. He got more evidence from his observations of the planet Venus. The Catholic Church believed that humankind, and therefore the Earth, was the centre of the universe. A teacher called Giordano Bruno had already been burned at the stake, in 1600, for saying that the Earth moved round the Sun. Galileo tried to get round the Church's censorship by publishing, in 1632, a book called *The dialogues concerning the two chief systems of the world*. This book was an imaginary argument between two great astronomers defending their views about the solar system. One supported the old view that the Earth was central; the other believed that the Sun was at the centre. Galileo carefully quoted evidence to support his own idea, the Sun-centred system, but seemed to agree with the Earth-centred view. Galileo escaped burning, but he was forced to deny his ideas about the solar system and go into exile.

Galileo

a What advantages did Galileo have compared with Copernicus?

b What is a modern view of the solar system? Write an explanation for a children's science magazine. You must explain:
– day and night,
– the seasons,
– year length,
– the way the planets move around the Sun.

c Imagine you are Galileo. Write part of his book, *The dialogues*. It should give evidence for the Earth being at the centre and for the Sun being at the centre.

d Why do you think people took so long to accept the idea that the Sun is the centre of the solar system? Think of as many reasons as possible.

e In 1492 Columbus risked his life by sailing west from Europe to try to reach India. Many Europeans thought he would fall off into space, because they believed the world was flat. What evidence and arguments could Columbus use to show that the world is not flat?

f What extra evidence could we use nowadays?

48.1 Nice sundial, pity about the Sun

 Never look directly at the sun.

Blagness Echo

Mayor's Sun stroke

In an attempt to change its image as the coldest, greyest town in Britain, the east-coast resort of Blagness has announced a £20 000 competition to design a giant sundial for its promenade. The Mayor said 'This is a chance for an up-and-coming British sculptor to become really well known. We are offering a central site on the sea front, and the council will pay the full construction costs. Contact the Town Hall for further details.'

You need:
– materials to build model sundial

a Prepare a design for the Blagness sundial. You will need to think about:

- What size and shape of pillar will give the best shadow?
- What should the pillar look like?
- Where should the scale markings go?
- How does the height of the Sun in the sky affect the length of the shadow?

Your competition entry must include:
– a detailed model of the sundial,
– short notes to show that you understand how the sundial will work,
– suggestions of suitable materials for making the sundial.

48.2 Measuring time

Measuring time depends on regular, predictable changes. We count how often these changes occur between two events and that gives us an idea of how far apart in time the two events are.

a Look at the timing systems shown on this page. For each one explain what the regular change is that people have used to measure time passing.

b Keep a diary of any changes you notice in the Sun and Moon over a period of a few days. Explain how people could use these changes to keep track of time.

c Explain how the Earth's movement affects:
– the length of the days and of the years,
– the height of the sun in the sky,
– the seasons.

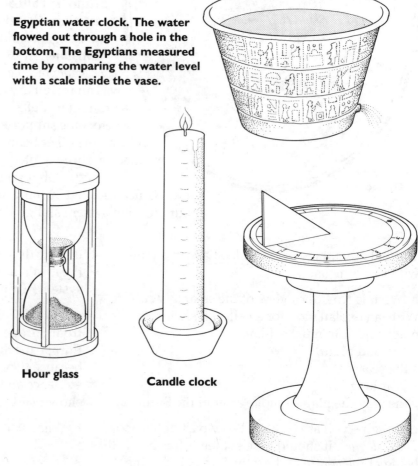

Egyptian water clock. The water flowed out through a hole in the bottom. The Egyptians measured time by comparing the water level with a scale inside the vase.

Hour glass

Candle clock

Sundial

KS 3 Assessment Activities Pack A

49 Space

49.1 Be properly addressed ...

a Put these words in order with the smallest region first:
- town
- galaxy
- country
- continent
- universe
- planet
- street
- solar system

49.2 The first step

The giant Saturn V rocket lifts Apollo 11 off the launch pad exactly on cue. Over the next 12 minutes, the rocket will burn nearly three million kilograms of fuel. It will enter orbit at over 28 000 km/h and, after two circuits of the Earth, a small burst of the engine will start the journey towards the Moon ...

a The radio commentator says the rocket will burn nearly three million kilograms of fuel. Why does it need so much fuel?

b Do a sketch of the forces on the rocket just before it goes into orbit.

c Once the spacecraft is in orbit, it needs much less fuel to push it towards the Moon than it did to get into orbit. Explain why.

d The drawing shows the path the rocket takes to the Moon. After the point X, the spacecraft starts to accelerate, even though no rocket engines are switched on. Explain why this happens.

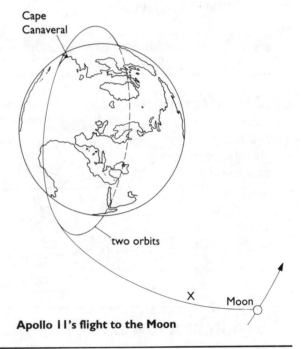

Apollo 11's flight to the Moon

49.3 Journey back to the beginning of time

It is AD 2205. Engineers have just managed to build a time machine that works. You are the first time traveller, and the count-down clock is running down to zero. In ten seconds, you will be catapulted by an enormous burst of energy back to the beginning of the universe – the big bang!

Write a short description of what you see on your journey. It could be:
- a script of the conversation between you and your mission control,
- a press release, after your return, describing your experiences and feelings,
- a diary of the events you see at the beginning of everything.

50.1 Going rotten

All of these bags claim to be biodegradable. Biodegradable means that microbes in the soil can destroy the bag.

Waste disposal experts want bags that rot as quickly as possible.
Choose one of the questions below:
– Does a whole bag decompose at the same speed as many little bits?
– Does a bag rot faster if the soil is hotter?
– Does burying a bag deeper in the soil help it to decompose?

Investigating

For the question you have chosen:

a Plan an investigation to find out the answer.

b What would you expect to happen?

c Why do you think that?

50.2 Coffee paper

You need:
– selection of papers
– filter funnel
– stand and clamp
– ground coffee
– supply of boiling water ⚠

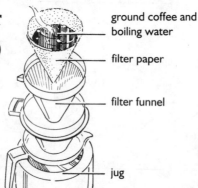

ground coffee and boiling water

filter paper

filter funnel

jug

Investigating

a What sorts of paper work best in a filter coffee machine? Design and carry out a test on four different sorts of paper.

50.3 Kitchen towels

Most people use paper kitchen towels to mop up spills and clean things in their kitchens. Think about the sorts of things that *you* would want to do with a kitchen towel.

Investigating

a Plan an investigation to find out which of the towels your teacher gives you is best. First, you must decide what you mean by 'best'. You can use any of the apparatus you are given. You may not need to use it all. Choose the apparatus to suit your investigation. Get your teacher to approve your plan and carry it out. Make a clear record of what you do as you go along.

b When you have finished, write a brief account of your investigation. Make sure you say what you have found out.

KS 3 Assessment Activities Pack A

50.4 Spreading far and wide

Bad news: you have got to paint your bedroom.
Good news: you can choose the paint.

a How will you decide how much paint to buy?

> **GPT's Super-silky emulsion**
> One litre covers 12 m² of a smooth non-porous surface.

Investigating

Plan an investigation to answer one of the questions below.

b How does the type of surface (wallpaper, bare plaster, brick) affect the amount of paint needed?

c Is cheap paint more expensive in the end because you have to use more of it?

d Which makes paint cover more wall: a roller or a brush?

If you can, carry out your investigation.

50.5 Party time

Billy is having his fifth birthday party tomorrow. He is helping his big sister to make the jelly and custard for the trifles. He watches as she carefully tears the jelly into small lumps.

'Why are you doing that?' he asks.

His sister pretends she didn't hear and adds the pieces to boiling water.

'Why are you using hot water? It won't work unless you put it in the fridge now! You don't know what you're doing! I'm telling mum!'

You need:
– jelly
– stopwatch or stopclock

Investigating

a Do you think Billy's sister is right to use small pieces of jelly and hot water? Explain why you think that.

b Design an investigation to test your prediction. Ask your teacher to check it, then carry it out. Write up and explain your results.

50.6 Soggy lawns

When it rains, the water lies on top of my lawn like a pond. When I look at other lawns, the water seems to drain straight through them. They always look good!

The local park keeper told me that the reason is that the soil under my lawn must have a lot of clay in it. Clay doesn't allow water to drain away quickly. He said that the rate at which water drains through soil depends on the composition of the soil. A sandy soil drains quickly but a clay soil does not.

Investigating

Plan an investigation to find out about the rate at which water drains through a mixture of sand and soil. How does the rate depend on the proportion of sand in the mixture? Get your plan checked by your teacher and carry it out.

Use any of the apparatus you have been given. You may not need not need to use it all. Choose the apparatus to suit your plan.

Make a clear record of your results as you go along. When you have finished, write a brief account of your investigation and explain your results.

50.7 Landslide!

Investigating

You need:
– tray
– sand and soil
– protractor

There are many piles of waste around Britain. Sometimes these piles are very dangerous. Use a sand tray to investigate how stable a pile of sand is. Try to answer these questions:

a What is the steepest stable slope for dry sand?

b How does the water content of the sand affect your answer to a?

c Is soil more stable or less stable than sand?

d Make a list of factors that you think determine the stability of a pile of a material.

KS 3 Assessment Activities Pack A

50.8 Downhill racer!

Investigating

Bill and Phil both have helter-skelters in a fun fair. Bill gives his customers a doormat to sit on when they slide down. Phil uses a piece of old carpet. They are both looking for a better material for their mats.

a Carry out an investigation to see which of the materials, you have been given, would be best in both wet and dry conditions. Use weights to represent a person on the slide.

b Look very carefully at the materials you tested. Explain why some materials were better than others.

c Now try *one* of these further investigations:
● Find out how the weight on the mat affects the speed of the mat.
● Find out how the slope of the slide affects the speed of the mat.

d Bill always gives his customers a push to start them off. Why do small customers need a smaller push than bigger ones?

e Sketch someone on the helter-skelter.

● Draw the forces that affect the person travelling down the track.
● Draw the forces that affect the person when he or she has stopped at the bottom of the slope.

f Write a sentence to explain each of these words:
– friction,
– gravity,
– weight.

50.9 Coffee cups

Ashok and Jane were buying cups of coffee from a stall at the fair. They noticed that, at one stall, the cups were plastic and, at another, polystyrene. Both stalls gave them a lid to keep their coffee warm.

They decided to do an investigation like one they had done at school. They wanted to find out which was more important for keeping the coffee warm:
– the type of material used for the cup,
– using a lid.

Investigating

a Which do you think is more important for keeping the coffee hot:
– the material the cup is made from, or
– whether it has a lid or not?

b Plan and carry out an investigation to find out if you were right. Get your plan checked for safety first.

c How does the lid help to keep the coffee warm?

KS 3 Assessment Activities Pack A

Collins Educational, 77–85 Fulham Palace Road,
London W6 8JB
An imprint of HarperCollins*Publishers*

© Richard Gott, Gareth Price, Tony Thornley 1992

First published 1992

ISBN 0 00 327476 4

Designed by Wendi Watson and AMR

Artwork by John Booth, Hardlines, Sally Neave and Rodney Sutton

Cartoons by Kate Shannon-Darby and Rodney Sutton

Printed in Great Britain by Loader Jackson Printers

The authors and the publishers are grateful to the Consumers' Association for
permission to adapt the table on page 41 from *Which?* magazine and to Lego UK
Limited for permission to use the diagrams on page 79.